Life and Times of Dasism Lord

By

Dion A. Smith Sr., M.A.

Dedication

This journal of the Life and Times of Dasism Lord is dedicated to my brother, Ralph Smith II, for being the strength I needed when I was weak. Everything I have done since your death has been for me and you. I dedicate this book to my best man Michael James for showing me how to navigate a hard knock life. You and your brother are the truth, rest in peace. Thank you both for letting me in and teaching me how to hold my own. Shout out Valley Boys OG Wheaty and OG Trell. My OG was JD. To the big Homies that didn't see me but I saw you...CCA Bob, Josey Wells, Rob J, Pokie, P Diddy, Pookie, Circle Boys, 20 Block, Will $crilla, and my 16th family. To my fallen friends and family who give me life... Johnelle Dixion, Dirshon Barnes, Ramone Larkin, Kris Davis, and Thomas Jackson. RIP Steve, Bub, Feet, King Domo, Kima, Rell, Wolf, Boo, Loco, Tyana, Smoke, Snoop, Jhonny, and Jose'. And if I have forgotten any of my fallen soldiers blame it on my memory and not my heart! I miss you all. This is for us...

ACKNOWLEDGMENT PAGE

I would like to acknowledge my mother for being my everything. She and I have gone through the fire and emerged like a phoenix out of the ashes. My mother is the strongest yet most humble person I know. I would like to thank you for allowing me to follow my own path and chase my dreams. My mother has provided me with just enough freedom that has made it possible to be who I am. I will continue to be an inspiration and motivation to all those I come in contact. I'd like to acknowledge my father for working to build a relationship with me. Through our conversations I truly see where my drive, perseverance, and ambition originate. This book is a manual for my sons, D. A. Smith II, and R. G. Smith. I love you both very much!!! I've done all the grunt work so you 2 will never know struggle. I promise that. Lastly, I'd like to thank those who believed in my vision and supported the dream.

TABLE OF CONTENTS

MURDER
15 year- old in Indianapolis
Summer of my 16th year
Fall 96'- Indy balling
Winter 96'- Michigan City
Summer 97'
Peer Pressure
Trippy
Senior Year
The come up
Burnt
Legend of the Black Truck
Phoenix
Notorious
Demonstration
For the Love of Money
Time to Fly
College
KD
Mikeo
Why

Murder

Living in the city of brotherly love, no. I lived in the city of ballers, hustlers, prostitutes, drug addicts, bootleggers, petty thieves, gamblers and don't let me forget the killers. G.I. is where I resided. Gary, IN is a Midwestern city at the very northern point of Indiana, East of Chicago. Gary was known as the "Murder Capitol" for several years in the 90's. I have learned to fade into the background as I have gotten older, but the G will either put you in position or take you completely out of all your positions.

I've heard that the city wasn't all ways like it is today but all I've ever seen is getting over, trying to get over and failing to get over. Throughout my life I have had connections with the G; I have always been a nigga from the G. The city only seems to get worse year by year taking on a life of its own that is chaos and it cannot be controlled or policed.

I started seeing the glare of drug dealers at about fourteen years old, I started smoking weed that same year. Personally, I wasn't raised to hurt others physically or mentally but I must say the nature of my environment caused a dramatic change within me that I will attempt to document in this journal of Dasism.

I have lived in Gary, Indianapolis and Michigan City, Indiana. I moved around a lot as a youngster under extreme circumstances. My brother Ralph Smith was murdered on January 4, 1996. Two days before his murder my home was shot up by three masked men. My neighborhood was not the typical hot spot for drama. I lived on a quiet block on the East side of the G known as 16th; an old folks neighborhood that was contaminated by the presence of their grandchildren.

I was talking on the phone Jan 2, 1996 in the basement of my grandmother's house. The lady I'm writing about is grown and married now so I'll just call her Ms. Howard. I'm trying my best to get out of the friend bag with her and spitting my best 15 year old shit when what sounded like a 3rd world war zone erupted outside.

Naive' to real gangsta shit I had no clue what was going on at the time. To me what sounded like rapid clicks or someone knocking on an aluminum door with keys on their knuckles gave way to Ms. Howard, still on the phone, saying "they shooting up your house"! At the same time, my mom's started screaming at the top of her lungs like she'd been shot.

I ran out of the room to see my mom's looking up the steps with a gaze in her eyes and grabbing at her heart with her right hand. Realizing what's going on she lays on the steps screaming "Get down, Oh Jesus, Oh my God!" I hear my grandmother upstairs, hit the floor screaming and praying to God. Grandma was in the back of the house but her scream was so piercing I would have thought she was next to me. I could hear both my grandmother and my mom's crying out for the Lord to help us. I could hear the windows breaking and crashing to the ground upstairs.

There was a rusted older model white Ford Escort in the driveway. I heard the car's tires explode from being hit with gunfire. What seemed like an eternity of gun fire ended. The house filled with smoke, broken glass, fragments of wood, dry wall, metal and lots of holes in everything. The aluminum door that kept us safe all these years was pierced with bullet holes.

The window that I had often looked through had broken frames and missing pieces of glass. The refrigerator had a bullet stuck in it by the door to the freezer. The walls were riddled with holes. Around the holes, the paint or plaster was missing leaving empty spaces when there was once color. The couch had the stuffing sprinkled on it, around it and behind it.

The lazy boy had a hole in it on the headrest in the same spot my grandfather would have been seated had he still been alive. The TV was busted and thick pieces of glass lay on the floor. Picture frames were broken and out of place. Everything was everywhere. What happened to my home, I thought?

All the windows in the front of the house were broken. The front door once had about 20 flat glass panels inserted in slots that when opened, controlled the ventilation into the house. The panels opened and closed by way of a small crank inside the door. Every panel in the front door was fragmented or shattered laying both inside the door frame and outside on the front steps.

The front of the house looked like Swiss cheese. The yellow metal siding that was once smooth and vibrant now looked like the craters of the moon with pockets and dimples caused by the penetration of the multiple caliber bullets used to devastate my place of solace.

Once the police arrived the aftermath of what really occurred became slightly clearer. The house sit's at the top of a "T" intersection. There is not an alley behind the home. Their plan was to ambush the house from three different vantage points to exploit the damage. Bullet shell casings lay on the street in three distinct locations. One directly in front of the house on the sidewalk, another in the neighbor's driveway to the west, and the last in front of my driveway.

Two of the piles were of .9mm shells totaling around 30 each were on the east and west scatters of shell cases. A pile of .223 caliber shells lay in front of the home. Two of the gunmen were in the front of the house and the other was on the side.

A hate was instilled in my soul at that moment. An evil that had been deep seeded awoke. I was a helpless 15-year-old young man. I didn't own any guns. I didn't know who did this to us. My mother, grandmother, and I could have been murdered in our own home. I didn't know how, when, who, or where but I did know someone would have to die for this violation. I felt weak and angry. Enraged but humbled as I knew not what to be encountered.

I wasn't fucking with school after that point. Overnight I grew up. Two days after my house was shot up I was instructed to go to school. I walked out the house that morning as I would usually do but instead of going to school I went to my friend Tom's house. Tom had a mother that wasn't strict. She was rather laxed when it came to school attendance and weed smoking in her house. Tom's house is where I went to feel free.

I sat and talked to Tom about my house being shot up and smoked a blunt while listening to Bone Thugs and Harmony. Loco pulled up in his green four door Mercury Trio. We pass the blunt around and discuss who might have done it. I then learn that 2 other houses had been shot up the same night my house was shot. The three of us chopped it up for a min then Loco an I hopped in the Trio and dipped. At this point in time in my life Loco is my right-hand man. I can count on this nigga to nut up when I'm spooked or vice versa. We go hard and don't fear much.

We went to the Visual and Performing Arts School because that's where all the stuck-up girls are and they love us weed smoking, thug niggas. We picked up Mela and her girl then bent some blocks blowing blunts and driving around the city. We got food and talked about my house being shot. The day was seeming normal. We dropped her girl back off at school and got ready to take Mela to Roosevelt High School for basketball practice.

At the corner, as we were passing the high school, I saw two men in dark clothes and hoods. Gary was under a state of emergency in 1996. To combat the rampant murders and drug selling the state of Indiana decided an influx of 50 additional State Police would help. The State Police were very visible but it didn't stop, slow or remove anything in my neighborhood. As we passed the corner of the high school a State Police car going in the opposite direction passed the hooded men on the corner. We had to wait for the police to pass so we could turn the corner that the hooded men are standing. As we waited to turn left a white big body Oldsmobile was waiting at the intersection on the same corner as the hooded men. The State Police went pass. Gun shots rang out! The two hooded men began shooting at the Oldsmobile breaking the back window out. The car tried to pull off but lost control and ran into the railing dividing the sidewalk from the street.

I recognize the two masked men as my brother's friends. Loco and I saw the masked men run through the alley to a parked car blocks away. Instantly I got excited "They getting em"! "They getting them nigga's for shooting up my house! I knew they were going to get em! You see that shit? They bust they shit up! That shit was gangsta!"

We dropped Mela off at the side of the school and drove around to the front of the school to see the police surrounding the abandoned car that had just been shot up. We drove around the other side of the school and I saw the school bus loading the students who go to the Career Center. The Career Center was a school that taught kids trades like carpentry and automotive repair. My brother went to the Career Center. I saw him alive for the last time standing on the steps with the other students getting ready to load the bus.

I'd always wondered why Ralph went to school that day. I wasn't going back, that was for sure. My brother was a different kind of nigga. He was never scared of anything. He didn't worry about the consequences or repercussions of his actions. He was a live for the moment type of guy. I admired his manliness. He made things happen and held his head high always, in public. My brother was the person I wanted to be. My goal was for him to see me as an equal and for him to respect me as such. Loco and I bent a few more blocks spent off what we just witnessed. I'd just seen an up close and personal attempted murder.

We were on 10 and needed some killa so we went to the spot to get a sack of bud. Loco went in the spot and emerged with 2 tightly rolled blunts ready to smoke. As we pulled off we fired up the killa on our way back to the hood to tell the niggas what happened. We smoked 1 and a half blunts. I took the half smoked blunt piece and put it in the fold of my skull hat. The snow started to fall as we approached the block. We saw police cars and an ambulance in the hood. There were about 50 people standing outside the cul-de-sac.

Loco parked the car a block away and we walked up to the crowd. "What's going on around here?", I asked. "It's a dead body over there" someone said. Loco and I walked to the alley to get a better view. The police had taped off the front of the houses but the alley was open.

I walked up to see a body lying on the ground with snow as fluffy and white as powder cocaine surrounding the body. "That's Ralph" Loco chimed in. (To this day I cannot see my big brother lying there. I can see the body but not him.) "Bullshit that ain't him." I said. I go back to the front where the police have taped off the scene and I noticed the crowd growing.

I pushed my way through the crowd and police. "Son you need to stay back, this is the police line" the police man told me. "I'm trying to see if that's my brother". He grabbed my arm and told me if I tried to cross the line again I would be arrested for obstruction of justice. I snatched my arm back from the officer and told him "fuck that, I want to know if that's my brother".

The officer of the got dam law pulled his handcuffs out and told me to put my hands behind my back and arrested me. "I told you little nigga to stand there and wait. Now you're going to jail". As I struggled to plead my case I was thrown in the back of the police car and taken down to the 13th Avenue police station.

I reflected on my life on my way to jail. I remember thinking that within the last few days I have had my house shot up, I saw someone get shot at, I feel my brother is dead and I'm going to jail. I was greeted at the police station by the familiar face of Officer Austin. Austin was a bullshit ass school cop who made high school more difficult than it needed to be because I wore braids and my pants were saggy.

Before my brother died I didn't do much more than skip school and smoke weed. He looked at me and said "I knew I see you here". They began to process me. They took off my coat and went through every pocket and rip. They patted me down and went through my pants pockets.

I was told to remove my shoes and socks. I was told to flip my socks inside out and put them back on. The officer then grabbed the skull hat off my head. My heart dropped to my stomach because I'd forgotten but I now remember that I have a half of blunt in my hat. I kept a poker face. Dam could he smell it, because I smell it now.

I thought about the stories I'd heard from the old heads about taking contraband into the jail and how you would get more time for the offence. Then I thought fuck it, I'm in here anyway. The officer squeezed my hat into a ball and passed it back to me in a tight ball as if he didn't want the blunt to fall out either.

I was harassed about my age because I was 15 at the time but I was about 6'4" and the officers wouldn't believe I was under 18. After a long debate about my birth date I was placed in a holding cell.

The cell was more of a small gapped fence which went from floor to ceiling with a door that locked in the middle. There was a window in the cell that had a view of the loading dock so I could see who was coming to jail. The carpet was a burgundy speckled piece of shit with holes from wear and tear. I sat on the wooden bench that stretched from one end of the cage to the other.

The bench was personalized with names, five-point stars, six-point stars, scratches, and broken parts of the bench splintered with age. The blunt in my hat was making me nervous because they may still find it, so I figured I would eat it. I had seen on TV so it's got to work, right? Well let me be the first to tell you that a burnt swisher sweet blunt with weed is not food and that shit made me gag. I chewed it twice before gagging. Having to formulate a new plan I chose to rub it into the carpet until nothing was left but a mark on the rug.

I sat there thinking about my life and if that was my brother who was on the ground being blanketed with a snow cover. An officer came to my cell and told me he would take me back to the scene. On the ride back to my neighborhood the officer told me that they found out it was my brother and they would not put me through more than I needed to go through, I was free. The officer told me to watch myself as he dropped me off at the site of my brother's murder. The crowd had dispersed by this time and I found myself alone.

The snow had grown to about a foot. And I had to walk three blocks in the dark. I knew not who killed my brother. I knew not who shot my house up and here I was alone and scared. The hardest person I knew in my life had been slain in the street blocks from our home. I manned up and walked down the snowy street placing every foot step into the tracks that the cars had formed in the street.

One block into my journey I see a car swerving up and down the street coming towards me. They make a left and go up the block, easing my nerves. The snowflakes were so large it made it difficult to see the houses in front of you. Then the car came back down the block spinning its tires and sliding from side to side in the street. My heart jumped and I panicked. I started running to my house afraid that this is my brother's assailants coming back to finish me off.

I got to my house, rang the bell and started knocking on the door. No answer. I beat on the door. No answer. I have lived in that house for years and my grandmother has always been here. This house has always had someone in it, always. But since the house was shot up she moved in with my aunt. My mother works and hadn't made it home yet. I had nowhere to go and my brother who would have made everything better was gone. I was the only one in my family who knows my brother was dead.

I gathered my courage to leave because the car is now coming back fishtailing from one side of the street to the other. They did a donut and gunned the engine towards me as I was walking back down the street. I wanted to make it to my friend Tattoo's house. The car turned up the block and I ran all the way to Tattoo's house. I knocked on the door and he answered. Tattoo had a cool family. The kind of family that would let you skip school at their house and smoke weed. As I went down the stairs I noticed Tom was in the basement. Tom was selling a little weed at the time. We were learning the game and could never cop more than a half an ounce at a time. Tom had just re-upped and had a fresh half ounce and a couple packages of swisher sweet blunts. We started talking about my brother being dead and smoking. I cried a lot that night.

I attempted to call my aunt. I wanted to let her know to call my mother and tell her Ralph was dead. She answered the phone and I was so shaken and terrified of what had occurred I could not get it together long enough to complete a sentence. I don't know why but my aunt told me to "get yourself together before you call me back, I don't have time for this" and hung up the phone. I cried so hard because I didn't know what to do. Who am I to tell? I felt so alone.

We smoked Tom's whole half ounce. Then someone knocked at the door. It was one of my brother's friends. I knew and trusted him. He asked me to ride with him. I agreed and left Tattoo and Tom. I was taken to the Color Doors housing project. We went into the home that was so thick with smoke it was layered in the air like waves in the lake. The smoke had grayish hue and a pungent aroma. There were five older men in the room and the two shooters I'd seen earlier on the corner of the school.

On the table were two pistol grip shot guns and two long barrel shot guns. There were several pistols and two SKS rifles. One of the shooters passed me the blunt and told me they were going to give me my brother's gun. I was told they were not going to let this slide and someone was going to die for my brother. I was passed a box of bullets then shit got weird. Naïve of all things gangsta until the day before yesterday, I started telling the shooter that I was there this afternoon. I told him I saw it all and that shit was right. He grabbed me and began to shake me. "You ain't see shit" Naïve, yeah, I saw you and him on the corner. Shaking me more "you ain't seen shit did you"? This went on for five or six more times until I understood I didn't see shit. I was dropped off at my house and they waited until someone answered the door.

My mother was home and she had no clue what had happened and I had the obligation to inform her that her oldest boy was dead. I asked my mother to take a seat because I had something to tell her. My mother was used to hearing dreadful things about us so she'd put up a defense to anything that sounded bad and told me to just tell her. I asked her to take a seat and again she refused my plea and screamed at me to "Tell Me"! I told my mother that "Ralph is dead". Her eyes got big as if a piece of her soul was removed from her at that very moment. She grabbed her chest. Screamed "NO"! Then she began hitting me with balled fists with a fury asking, "What did you do?" The rest of the night is a blur but I do know it was long.

The next week continued to open my eyes to the previously veiled world of the underground. I had never held a gun before last week and now I had my very own sawed-off barrel, .22 rifle with the short stock. It was fabricated with a wide black PCV pipe around the barrel so it looked like a shot gun a first glance. I kept it on me in my pants leg with the stock strapped to my waist by my belt. I would walk with a stiff leg.

My crew was about 5 deep and they were showing me more respect than ever. I was approached by the dope man one night. Me and my niggas were at the chicken joint. I was standing outside watching everything moving as I did at that time.

He pulled up in a candy blue Cadillac Seville with a white quarter rag with the gold bullets around it, the wheels were gold Dayton's with eagle spinners. The window rolled down and he called me over. "You got some money in your pocket". I replied "No." "Prove it," he said. I flipped out my pockets to reveal nothing. He pulled out a dope man knot and peeled off $100. "You know where my spots at? Come through there on Monday and I'm a put you on. You ready for that"? I replied "This is what I been waiting on".

My brother's funeral was on that Saturday and it was the largest funeral I have ever witnessed to this day. The funeral home overflowed with people. The students from school poured out the door. I understood then, that it is the memory that you leave that will outlast your body.

The procession of cars stretched for over a mile as we caravanned to the cemetery. I was told after the funeral that I would be moving to Indianapolis tomorrow. I was blindsided. I didn't want to move. I had a gang, a gun and I was about to get on. What the fuck! I protested and was told it was for my safety. My things were packed and I was driven to Indianapolis to live with my aunt.

15-year-old in Indianapolis

The ride to Indianapolis from Gary took about 2 ½ hours. My mother didn't like to drive anywhere so this trip was a step out on faith for her. Moms rented the smallest car she could which left my 15 year old 6'4" frame balled up in the front seat. The trip was further complicated by the fact that I had the sawed-off .22 rifle strapped to my waist and down my right leg which caused me to have to sit with an extended leg the whole ride. I would have to shift and adjust myself every 20 or 30 miles. By the time we entered the Indianapolis city limits my leg was numb. Moms never noticed my leg abnormally stretched out as we made our way to my aunt's home.

Aunt V, cousin Na' and her boyfriend Big greeted us upon our arrival to their home in which I was to stay. Na' is my first cousin and my heart. Na' was the only female guide I had growing up that understood this street shit and would school me to getting bitches and shit. Na' is about 5'10" cinnamon brown skin, brown eyes, shoulder length midnight brown hair with a brick house frame. Her boyfriend Big is a 6-foot dark skinned 300 pound linebacker framed nigga from the G. We all greet and I am shown my room. I immediately put the chopper under the mattress for safe keeping and put my things away. Moms left me some money, made sure I was alright and went back to the G.

In the morning, my aunt told me we needed to go to the school to enroll. We walked to the bus stop on High School Rd. and waited for the bus to take us the school. Nap was different than the G as I noticed all the traffic going up and down the 6 lane streets. Everyone seemed to be in a rush and had important things to do compared to my aunt and I waiting on a bus. We boarded the bus that would take us down street to North West High School. The school was enormous. We entered the office and was seated in a little office with a clerk who told me that I could go to any school in Nap. I could choose. I had no clue of how the city was broke down but I saw a map of the schools and I picked the school the furthest from the house. I chose Broad Ripple High School. I lived on the Northwest Side of Nap in an apartment complex off of 38th and High School Rd. I went to a school on the other side of town.

On the first day of school the temperature was cold outside so I wrapped myself in a triple fat goose to keep me warm. I left out the apartment and approached the bus stop. I noticed a short dark-skinned male with corn rolls to the back standing next to a gate by the bus stop. I spoke, nodded my head, and told him I was new in town. I told him I wanted to know what it was to do for fun. He told me his name was Troy. Troy then began giving me the spill about our part of town. The bus stop filled up with about 15 people as he told me the ins and outs. Troy was telling me about the bitches when the bus pulled up.

I noticed the females standing around so I made sure to talk a little louder about how I was from the G. I saw the yellow school bus come around the corner with blacked out tinted windows a white roof with a flashing light on the top. I had never seen a school bus like that in the G before, everything is different in Nap. We loaded the bus and went to the back to finish the conversation. I found out I was now living in Murder Ville a completely G.D. folks section of Nap.

I am, was and will forever be an Insane Vice Lord (IVL) till I die and this was disturbing information he was telling me. I listened to the jewels he was dropping on me and soaked up what was being said with no emotion being expressed on my face. I felt that I would be alright as long as I had my chopper. I would make sure I kept it on me always when I was in the neighborhood walking around. Troy had no clue I was a Lord and he wouldn't for now, I didn't want any trouble, I just wanted to know the business.

My few months at Broad Ripple High were intense. I was trying to fit in but I could not get comfortable with the new unfamiliar environment. I was the new kid and I stood out like a sore thumb because of my height. I'd lost my barber and my brother together as he cut my hair. My brother would line my edges and even out my afro. My hair wasn't long enough to braid so I would get the hot comb in the morning and blow it out.

The school day came and went. On the bus ride home I asked Troy where the weed was at and I was invited over his house to smoke a blunt. Troy's family lived in the section of the complex that had town homes. His house was nice and full of expensive things. I was fresh out the G where all my friends didn't have a father in the home. The people I knew in the G were barely making it and I saw something different in his home for the first time in my life. I thought to myself dam they getting it out here. Troy pulled out a Swisher Sweet blunt and rolled up a fatty.

He invited some of his friends over. A thick ass dark skinned female with skin tight jeans and two light skinned male twins with curly hair came to the house. We smoked and talked. I told them about the G. I got to Nap in 96 when the G was Murder Capitol of America so I was asked a lot of questions about how it was to live in a place so dangerous. I could only tell them it was not like that if you live it every day of your life. From the outside looking in it may seem like a place where you walk out the door and get shot. Hell, it's possible but it's life. I shared tidbits of information about where I was from and how it was and they shared stories about Nap. I was told that most girls here are easy and if you smoke a blunt with them they'll fuck. As I left his house high as a kite a blue Chevy Tahoe pulled up with three men inside. The men looked at me with a stone face, mug on mean, look as they called Troy over to the truck. I noticed the harsh look but I wasn't feeling fear. I had my chopper down my leg as I had gotten use to carrying it and not being noticed by anyone. I walked home.

The next day at the bus stop I saw Troy. I greeted him with a hand shake. I asked Troy if he could plug me with his weed connection. He told me he would talk to me after school then began talking to one of the females at the bus stop. I hated school. Broad Ripple was the biggest school I had ever seen in person. The school was the size of 4 Roosevelt high schools put together. The halls were wide but walking through the halls was shoulder to shoulder. I was tall at the age of 15 so I could see over the crowd of people. I was awkward and self-conscious of the constant stares and questions of how tall I was or the size of my feet.

Mom's was sending money weekly so my clothing game stepped up to Nike suits and Jordan shoes. Big was balling so I had access to his gold rings, bracelets and herringbone chain which I adorned to appeal to the bitches loving ballers. I had the swag of a baller but I wasn't slanging shit. I sat in every class that day daydreaming of getting home so I could smoke a blunt, kick it with Troy and hope he invited that thick chick back over.

When we got home that day I asked Troy again if he could plug me with the connection. I was told he would meet me at my house and we would take a walk and smoke a blunt. Troy came to the house about an hour later and we walked to the edge of the complex. The apartment complex was right next to the highway. There was a large drainage pipe that traveled under the highway from one side to the other. The pipe was massive enough to drive a truck through. We had enough room to be comfortable in the tube. We entered the corrugated metal tubing and walked to the middle. Troy fired up the blunt and the sound of cars and trucks rumbling could be heard over head. Troy inhaled several short tokes and told me that big folks didn't want him hanging out with me anymore.

He told me that when I left his home the day before the people in the truck were Big Folks and them and they noticed I was wearing my hat to the left. Troy looked me in my eye and asked me, as if he wanted a different answer, if I was a Vice Lord. I looked Troy back in the face as cold as I could and told him, I was. He told me if I was going to be living out here I would have to flip to folks. As we smoked and talked a short, dark toned, Hispanic man with blue jeans, and a left pant leg ripped at the knee, entered the pipe from the far end loaded with grocery bags. We clenched the metal ribbed wall to grant passage to the man, as if we were the keepers of the tunnel, as he passed. I told Troy my brother was just killed by so called fellow members of his clique and there was no way in hell I would ever flip to folks. He told me that if I didn't flip he wouldn't be able to hang with me. I couldn't believe how we'd been cool up to this point and Big Folks and them made him change on me. As we walked out the pipe I felt alone again and in a sense of danger. Troy never talked to me again.

I saw Troy every day I caught the bus to school and never got acknowledged after that day. He would just talk to the girls. I would stand there, looking stupid. Some of the girls on the bus stop were sexy as hell but I couldn't bring myself to spit game at them. I missed my classes at break a bitch college. I never knew what to say and I would just be spitting stupid nonsense. I hated standing on that bus stop.

My first class of the day was a three-hour block of electronics. I liked the guys in that class because most of them were seniors and only the seniors could leave the campus for lunch or drive to school. One of the guys would take orders early in the morning and sneak over to McDonald's during class to get breakfast. Because I looked as old as the seniors I would sneak out with them. I'd just lie if anyone asked what grade I was in.

Once they found out I smoked weed, we would leave on lunch hour and smoke a blunt while circling blocks. These guys took that electronics shit serious. They would spit wattage an ohm percentage like they were bible verses and I would just shake my head like I knew what the hell they were talking about. I just liked the beat in the car but could give two fucks about how it worked. I learned to play my role and get in where I fit in.

I didn't like any of my other classes. I hated lunch hour if I had to stay in the building. I never had a true group of friends so I would just sit at the lunch table looking out of place not talking to anyone. I never ate because I didn't want to stand in line and have people staring at me.

I wanted to fit in and be a part of something but everything seemed so complicated and awkward. I spent 2 months going to a drama class because I didn't read my schedule correctly, neither did the teacher. She just added my name to the attendance list. When I finally found out I was in the wrong class I felt stupid, real stupid. I should have been in the speech class.

Speech class was in a room at the back of the gym. We had to walk through the stadium doors and go through the gym to get to the class. This class was full of thugs and loose white girls. We never got anything done because of constant disruptions by the thugs talking shit and loose white girls making out with the thugs in the corner. I saw more ass and tits in that class than I did my whole time in Nap. I wanted to be down so much that I became a follower. I'd always had my niggas with me. I was never alone at school, until now. Looking back, I needed my niggas with me to feel like a man.

One of the guys in speech class came up with the idea of punching white boys after class. I took this as my opportunity to prove myself. Four of us would line up against the wall at the entrance of the gym before you entered the stadium door. The plan was for the first person in the line to hit a white boy and everybody else would get a lick in. As we saw our victim approach he carried a book bag and was minding his business going to his next class. He was tall with blonde hair and blue eyes. The first guy in line, on our white boy bashing squad, hit him square on the jaw. The white boy was hypnotized with one punch and fell to the ground. The other three of us ran up, leaned over and hit him a couple of times then ran off through the crowd. We would switch up every day on who'd take the lead on the white boy bashing line. Every day of that week we picked out an unsuspecting victim and beat him to the ground and ran away. On Monday of the next week when we tried to resume our game but there was an announcement made on the intercom right after

Speech class warning students and staff that there had been several beatings in the hallway by the gym. The announcement told the staff to provide supervision in the hallway. That was the end of that.

My last class of the day was wood shop. This class was fun but once again it was filled with knuckleheads. I was learning things in the class like making things out of wood. I liked using the machines like the lay. The class was rather open with lots of space to move about. There was probably too much space.

Guys in class would pop firecrackers and throw them at the teacher from behind the tables that gave great cover. The teacher would hit the deck like he was having flashbacks from war. This would go on all class period sometimes. The teacher would get his shit together, regaining his low level of composure, then try to help someone with a project then, Pop, Pop, Pop, Pop. I believe the wood shop teacher was kind of slow or he was getting close to retirement because he allowed all the foolishness we would put him through.

One of the most vivid memories of wood shop class was the one time I was suspended from school for something I didn't do. In wood shop, there was always a bin of wood scraps of assorted sizes in a pile. On this particular day, the teacher was at the chalkboard trying to explain something.

Every time he would turn his back someone would throw a piece of wood at him. The teacher would cower, throw his hands above his head for protection and ask who did it. This happened about 4 times to the point where he would just turn to the side, keeping one eye on the class and the other on the chalk board, because he was paranoid. That was the funniest thing to me and every time he would cower I would burst into laughter, the shit was pure comedy.

By the fourth time he was hit he would holler out my name, like I did it, because I was laughing the hardest and loudest. At the end of class we lined up at the door as usual. Big Black, had been throwing the wood at him all class, grabbed an arm full of wood scraps as we stood by the door. When the bell rang we piled out the door.

Big Black went through the door and as soon as he passed the threshold he threw the wood behind his back. I was standing behind Big Black so when the avalanche of wood fell on the teachers head he assumed it was me. The next day I was suspended for 10 days.

The bus trip home from school was always long. I'd be on the bus for over an hour and a half. I sat in the back with the trouble makers, where the fun was. I couldn't wait to go home especially since I was locked in the school all day with no fresh air. We would sit in the back of the bus and smoke squares and blow the smoke out the window. We would smoke weed but we rarely had rolling papers or blunts so we would roll it out of notebook paper. It's surreal to think that we would pass a notebook paper joints across the aisle like it was all good. We smoked in the back of the bus more times than not.

We were caught one afternoon and it's ironic that we were caught smoking a square and not killa. One of the kids up front smelled the smoke and told the bus driver "somebody smoking crack, I smell it". No one was smoking crack but it caused the driver to stop the bus and call the police. We sat there forever until the police pulled up. All the police did was asked if anyone had anything they shouldn't because he was going to check. Nobody in the back said a word and no one in the front had seen who was smoking so they couldn't finger point. The police officers super bluff was called out and he did nothing. The police warned the bus that if they got another call "someone is going to juvie".

I needed a new plug on the killer because I needed to smoke on a daily. I was met by a guy named CD who stopped me in the parking lot of my apartment complex. CD had mix tapes and bootleg CD's for sell. CD also had the plug on the weed. He gave me his number and told me to call him when I needed something but he wouldn't come out of the house for less than $20. I bought a couple of CD's and a bag of killa. I was feeling self-sufficient again and calm because I had found my own plug and I didn't need Troy to help me or Big Folks.

Super Bowl Sunday came and I called CD to bring me a half an ounce of bud. He took all day and I must have called his phone about 10 times before he finally showed up at my door. I paid him what I owed and he left. Big and I were ready for a Super Bowl feast we had chicken wings, chips, dip, beer and the icing on the cake was the killa. My aunt had to work that day so I rolled up, sat in front of the TV and sparked up.

I was in the zone before I knew it feeling right almost to right. In the background we had Biggie Smalls "ready to die" playing. I was zoning hard off that killa. I was higher than I'd ever been before, I was tripping.

By half time the music got to talking to me, personally. I started hearing "kill him". "He won't even expect it, just do it". "Just do it". "Look at him sitting over there, kill him". I had never in my life felt like I was feeling at that time. The voice was in a whisper with the confidence of persuasion. The voice would come through my ears and penetrate my brain with sharp jabs.

I tried to shake it off but the voice just got louder. "Kill him". I felt sick to my stomach and started sweating. I became violently ill and had to run to the bathroom to throw up. The room got to spinning and all types of thoughts of murder floated around my head. I made it to the room and closed my eyes. I was confused by the voices and visions swirling in my head.

I laid down in the bed and curled up in the fetal position. Random thoughts and visions were popping around in my head like cold water on hot grease. I missed the last half of the game and told Big to stay away from me for his own good. I didn't know what was going on and I didn't want him to find out, if I lost it. Big dismissed my actions and went on watching the game and going about his day.

When I awoke in the morning I told Big I never wanted to hear Biggie ever again in my life because the song was giving me subliminal messages. To this day I don't know why I had those thoughts while listening to that song. I have since listened to his music high than a mother fucker and I have not had those thoughts. I came to the realization that my weed was laced with something. I learned quickly that I would never buy weed from someone that I didn't know.

When the weather broke in the spring I'd learned a little about Nap and felt more comfortable getting around on my own. Big worked at the CVS on the corner and would get me 40's of Ole E to keep me popped off if I asked. I'd also found another connection on the weed through Big.

I hated Nap with a passion so getting high and drunk at night was a religious routine that kept me sane. Some nights I would wait to 2 or 3 in the morning, go outside and empty the clip of the .22 rifle. Shooting was the mental release I needed to deal with my life. Hearing the gun go off flooded a sense of power through my veins. Knowing there was someone inside of their home afraid of the shots made me feel like an important and feared person. Watching the reddish orange sparks explode from the gun when it's fired made me feel invincible.

I was with family but I never wanted to be there. I wanted to be in the G with my niggas getting paid. I made calls back to the G daily to see what was going on and what I was missing.

I embraced the love of a long-distance relationship with Ms. Brown Eyes. She kept my mind at ease. She tried to keep me out of trouble through conversation. I loved this girl and every time I could get to a phone I called her. I wanted her physically but I never hit, hell the most I ever did with her was finger that pussy.

She was such a crucial factor to my sanity in those days because she would accept my calls no matter what time I called. This young lady was mentally and sexually advanced compared to my experience. My bashful ways and long distance put me in the best friends' forever bag. All I wanted to do was leave this place and be back with my own kind.

I was out of touch with myself, my people, and my girl. Moms kept the money coming on a biweekly basis to make sure I wasn't a burden on my aunt. She was sending money faster than I could spend it, so I began saving it for a rainy day. Moms eventually moved to Nap right before summer break and we got an apartment away from Murder Ville.

We moved the U-Haul load of things she brought from the G into the new apartment that was on the second floor of Aspen Village. I hadn't brought my things from my aunt's home but I was told we'd get them later. I wasn't worried about anything but my chopper under the mattress. I spent the night on a bed that felt familiar. I awoke to a new scene and the sun shining through the window of my own room.

I was 16 years old and this was the first time in my life I had a room that was mine to close the door and protest if I wanted. No one had their things in my room but me. Wow, what a feeling! I thought this would be the change I needed. Moms was back and we were a family again.

I stayed busy for a week before I was able to get back to my aunt's house. I was greeted by Na' and asked about how I liked the new apartment. I obliged the conversation until I felt I had a chance to get to the room and gather some things. I played the whole demonstration out in my head for a week on how I would get the chopper out of the house undetected. I would wrap it in some clothes and go into the bathroom and strap it to my leg. I gathered the pants that would conceal the gun with one hand, I reached under the mattress with my other hand to scoop it in the pants leg, in one smooth motion. I didn't feel it, so I reached further back under the mattress but nothing. I dropped the pants and reached with both hands up to my elbows under the mattress to no avail. Sweat started to bead on my forehead and my heart started to pump. I thought to myself "What the fuck is going on"! I flipped the mattress over and to my surprise there was no gun. In disbelief and complete confusion, I went back into the living room where I'd left everyone else.

I asked Na' to step outside and talk to me for a minute. She came out and told me she knows why I look like that. She explained that her mother found the gun a few days after I moved when she was cleaning. Na' told me that auntie was changing the sheets and as a habit she flips the mattress when the sheets get changed. The gun was sitting under the mattress looking like a felony and visit from the police, so she threw it in the garbage. I couldn't believe or understand why she would treat my brother's gun like that. I did the only thing I could think of at the time. I went to the brown dumpster in the parking lot with fly's hovering above a week's worth of section A's garbage piled up. I jumped in. I was chest deep in other people's shit but I wanted and needed my gun back. I tossed bags, stepped on and ripped bags but no gun poked out. My gun, my brother's gun, was gone. I was alone again in this city of Folks naked to the world. I wasn't going to take this anymore. I was far from a child and it was my time to let my family know how I want to do things.

I walked back to Aspen Village contemplating my next move.

I'd been saving my money for something like a rainy day or whatever that meant. When my gun was thrown away I knew my rainy day would be on the last day of school. I waited for my moms to go to work early in the morning. She left hours before I had to go to school. She walked out the door when it was still dark outside and the birds were chirping loud. I looked from my window on the second floor to see her walk through the parking lot to the bus stop on the other side of the complex. It felt like an eternity for the bus to come into view. I watched it come from four blocks away catching every light. When the bus picked her up I stuffed my bag full of clothes, gathered the money I'd been saving and walked out the apartment to be on my own.

I went to the same bus stop she'd left from and caught the next bus on the route. The bus traveled through the city and ended up downtown. I exited the bus with my life on my back. I went to the Greyhound bus station across the street from the city bus terminal. I bought a one-way ticket back to the G.

Summer of my 16th year

Sitting on the bus I thought I would never come back to Nap. I thought I would go back to the G and become a kingpin. The overcast in the sky was a gloomy dark grey hue that grew more menacing the closer I got to Gary. The road became raggedy with potholes, uneven pavement and I started to notice missing street signs. I was home. I exited the bus and breathed in the air of the G which I had craved for so long. I knew that there is a vibe to the city and I would have to find my tune so I could play a note. There is an undertone, a rhythm that flows in the heart beat of the city. I was prepared to embrace the pulse and ride the wave. I called my nigga June at the bus station to come and get me. He picked me up and we talked about me running away and how I was about to sell dope.

June dropped me off at my grandmother's home. I hadn't seen the house since it had been ambushed. It was different than I remembered. Grandma put steel security doors with deadbolt locks on both entrances which guarded from a kick door. The roof was lined with security lights that shined florescent beams of daylight if triggered by motion on each side of the house. The whole home was fitted with new yellow siding and white framed windows. I walked up the green carpeted steps gently supporting myself on the rusted rod iron railing and rang the doorbell. Grandma came to the door. Her face was weathered yet supple. She was vibrant and had a glowing smile on her face. She appeared sun kissed. Her hair was black and shiny like silver, pulled to the back. She wore a full-length blue floral house shirt. Each step she made in her house shoes slid across the floor making a sliding scraping noise when she walked. We gathered around the wooden table that has been in the same place in the kitchen since I can remember. We sat and she asked what I was doing there. I told her I was going to stay the summer and my mom's said it was ok. Grandma didn't think twice about it and asked if I wanted something to eat. I told her yes. I settled in and plotted my next move.

I was on 10 to be back on the block and couldn't wait to kick it with the niggas. I had a little money in my pocket and was ready to find my peoples and get high. I went around the corner and saw my nigga Loco sitting in a brick colored bubble Chevy Caprice. Loco was about 6 feet tall and stocky. He wore thick braids and was the little brother of the Big Homie. He always had a look in his eye like he was up to something, but he was my nigga.

We slapped hands and threw up the pyramid. My nigga was insane to the brain and always had something to prove to someone. He took me to the weed spot to cop a sack and to the gas station for an Optimo green leaf blunt. We went back to the cul-de-sac on the block to roll up and politick.

I told my nigga I was back and I wanted to make some money. I told him I heard he was out here getting it and I wanted a piece. Loco hit the blunt and inhale deeply then told me his brother put him in position and I had to get in where I fit.

I needed a plug to get money. I thought I was where I fit in. Things had changed in the few months I'd been gone. My niggas were selling dope now and money was important. I didn't have time to find my role. This wasn't how it was supposed to happen. I planned on being plugged and blessed with a sack to sell. Later that day my nigga Vinnie pulled into the cul-de-sac because he'd heard I was back. Vinnie fired up a blunt and started asking me about what I was going to do. I told Vinnie I wanted to get on. Vinnie asked me if I was ready for that. I said "fo sho". Vinnie told me to meet him at the pink house on 19th and Virginia St. when I got some time. Vinnie finished the rest of the blunt he was smoking with us and pulled off.

We finished chopping it up and I had Loco drop me off at the pink house on 19th. When I walked in I saw faces I hadn't seen since my brother was murdered in the streets. Mikeo, Vinnie, Juggy, Beany, Murdoc, D.B, Feet and others were in the place. Refer smoke met me at the door as I shook everyone's hand ending with a pyramid to salute the Five and I embraced the love. I was lead to another room in the back by Vinnie and given a 16th of an ounce of crack. I'd never sold crack before and made money. I would steal my brother's dope back in the day and try to sell it to the crack head across the street but she would always get my dumb ass. I would end up giving it away for free if she told me a sob story or let me see a nipple "by accident". Vinnie sat me down and showed me how to chop the small rock up with a razor blade into 10 pieces of crack and stuff the rocks into #1 seals. The bags came in different colors and looked like tiny zip-lock bags. Vinnie told me to sell each one for $10 apiece. He told me to give him back $50 and the rest was on me. Vinnie told me he didn't give a fuck about how I made the money but any deals I made would come out of my money and not his. At the end of the pack he needed $50... no ifs, ands, or buts about it.

Vinnie told me that everybody in the spot got a turn at the door and that when it was my turn, make the money. I also learned that P was the owner of the spot and when he came in he got to make all the hits until his pack was gone. P was the dope man in the candy blue Caddy who offered me a position in the organization before I left to Nap. The spot was nothing special. It was a two-story home in the middle of a major avenue.

There was a large bay window in the front that allowed whoever was on lookout to view north, south and east. There was no furniture except for 4 chairs, a couch, table, TV and video game system. There was no dope sold out the front and foot traffic in the front was to be avoided unless we were coming and going. The back door was at the bottom of the steps. We had a doorbell in the back that would alert us to someone wanting some dope.

We could look out the window on the second floor in the back to see who was there and what they wanted. Someone would open the door if everything was cool and serve the geeker. This happened all day and night while we took turns on who would answer the door next.

I gave Vinnie his first $50 within the first hour. He gave me another 16th and within an hour I gave him back $50. Vinnie gave me an 8 ball for $100 and I was able to bag up $240 worth of $10 bags. I sat in the spot day and night making money. More money than I had ever seen in my life. Like clockwork every ten to twenty minutes the doorbell would ring and whoever was next up for the hit would step to the back and get paid.

While we waited for our next turn at the door we would play the game, smoke, drink and talk shit. It was nothing but love. I'd been in the spot for over a week straight. I had not been back to my grandma's house or washed my ass in that time. I was living the life of a hustler.

The doorbell rang. It was my turn so I ran to the back to get off the stones in my pocket. I got the ok and opened the door. There was a 30 something female standing there and she asked for Beany. I told her he was up there but it was on me. She asked again for Beany. I told her it was on me, so, what you want. She stepped in and closed the door behind her. She was dressed in light fitting brown dress that stopped in the middle of her thighs. The dress had spaghetti straps and a V cut that exposed her cleavage. She asked me to show me what I had. I pulled out 3 fat dime bags in blue #1 seals concealed in the palm of my hand. I opened my hand to display my work. She said "ohh them fat".

She then turned around looking me in the eye as she hiked her dress up to her waist exposing her perfectly bubbled ass cheeks. She bent over, grabbed her ass and shook it. My dick was throbbing and growing in my week-old underwear when she asked if I wanted to fuck her. She smacked her ass with one hand while holding the dress up with the other. She stood up and pulled out her sweat glistening breast and squeezed it. She pulled on her oversized chocolate nipple until it was erect. Her mouth opened and she began sucking her nipple in the doorway of the spot. I had never seen a woman so sexy in my life and my dick told me to fuck her. I told her "hell yeah" I want to fuck.

I brought her in the house and up the stairs to one of the rooms. I pulled my dick out, Feet came in the room. I had the bitch bent over a box, ass out, while my dick was throbbing with lust for that pussy. Feet stopped me. "You ain't got no rubbers? You can't fuck without no rubber D" Feet told me. I was so horny I really didn't give a fuck but he wouldn't let me do it without a jimmy. I left and hooped on the bike that we all used to run to the gas station or get something to eat. I peddled faster than I had ever in my life. I walked up to the counter inside the station and proudly asked for a rubber. Within an instant I was back at the spot with a hard dick ready to fuck. When I got back she was in the room sucking Feet's dick. I got behind her and began fucking. It was over before I got into it but it was a feeling I never got over. I now knew I could make a bitch do whatever I wanted for a hit of dope. I never saw that bitch again but she was my first piece of pussy. I lost my virginity to a dope fiend in a dope spot.

I stayed awake for 10 days straight while I lived off liquor, weed, bullshit food and the pure adrenalin of being in a dope house. I would be awake at night staring out the window watching the street. I was afraid if I went to sleep the police would kick in the door and I would be caught off guard. I wanted to see it coming. Jail wasn't in the plan so being as aware as I could was important.

A week and a half had passed before I decided I needed to sleep in a bed and wash my funky ass. I rode the bike back to the hood in the heat of the sun. I saw June and Loco on the corner sharing a 40 ounce of Ole Gold. My afro was matted to my head and I smelled like ass and onions. I was wearing the same clothes I'd came back to the G in and they smelled of weed, liquor and cigarettes.

I told them Vinnie put me on and I'd been in the spot on Virginia. I dug in my pocket and pulled out $2500. I had never seen or made that much money before in my life. I don't think they'd seen that much before in one fat ass dope man knot tightly bound by a red rubber band. June chimed in "You bumping D". I was but I didn't make it seem like a big deal.

We smoked a blunt on the corner and talked about the shit I'd seen while bumping in the spot. I joked about how much money was coming through the spot. I told June fuck bumping we quaking that bitch. The spot was making about $5,000 a day off $10 hits, on a bad day.

I got back to grandma's house and she was happy to see me. She was not worried about my whereabouts and didn't ask me any questions about my absence. She told me she'd talked to my mother and wanted me to call her. I didn't want to call moms because I knew the conversation would be for me to come back to Nap and how much of a burden I was being on her mother. I wasn't going to come back until I was ready. I washed my ass, got something to eat and got back in the streets.

I saw my nigga Crazy Curt. Curt was an O.G. and he knew my struggle and the fact that my brothers enemies were now mine. Curt was a real player. He gave me ride and we talked about what I was going to do about them niggas who killed my brother. He told me the niggas I was fucking with were soft and I shouldn't be around them because they don't think.

Curt asked if I had a gun because I couldn't be out here naked. Curt opened the glove box, reached in and passed me a brown workers glove. The glove was heavy. He told me that was for me. It was a 5 shot .22 revolver. Curt told me to never tell anyone where I got it from and never get caught with it because there was a body on it. Curt told me to take his number and call him whenever for whatever.

I went back to the spot and copped a 1/ 2 ounce for $400 and broke it down into $1000 worth of dime rocks. I was ready to rock and roll. The night came and since it was hot out everyone was outside and standing in front of the spot instead of being inside to keep attention away from what we had going on in the house. The group grew to about 20 people. We were all underage at the time but you couldn't tell by the way we lived on our own, carried guns and drank in public like it was legal.

An argument broke out about them standing in front of the spot selling dope in the open. It was about 2 in the morning and these niggas start yelling about not selling dope in public. Before you knew it they were down there fighting. A white Monte' Carlo peels off in the night. My niggas were still outside posted up when the car came back up the street at about 50 mph. Brock! Brock! Brock! These niggas start shooting at my niggas. I'm in the window watching the whole demonstration unfold. My niggas dipped in the cut, grabbed their choppas' and started busting back but by the time they fired a shot at them niggas…they were gone. The house took a couple of bullets but nothing major.

I left the spot after that night and I never went back. I spent the rest of the summer in the hood with my 16th niggas. I'd been missing them anyway. I liked making money but chilling with my niggas was what built me up to be more. We wasted time on a daily by drinking 40 oz. bottles of Ole English malt liquor, smoking weed, selling dope, and playing basketball at the court.

On this afternoon Playboy and I were at the court when Red, Norman, and Kevin came to the court. We got a 2 on 2 going and I started getting fouled. I'd call foul and they'd tell me to man up. Play after play I was getting fouled and I started fouling too. When they won the game I saw them huddle up and start talking. I didn't think much of it as I kept shooting the ball around.

June pulled up in his mother's Ford tempo. They ran over to June and started talking to him as Playboy and I continue to shoot around. Next thing I heard is "D! Hell naw that's my nigga!" They walked away from the car and June called me over and told me to roll with him.

I hopped in and he told me that they were going to jump me. Wow! Had I been so oblivious that I never saw or felt those niggas conspiring against me? Had they just asked my nigga to help? Why was they so mad? Thanks June for getting me out of there.

I'm a thinker, after almost being jumped I began to plot how I'd catch em. I'd find them. I'd make em pay. I'll me em respect my gangster. It was a few days later when Loco told me that he saw Red at summer recreation in the Pulaski middle school gym. I was ready. They didn't know me. They didn't know what they'd done but I was about to teach em all a lesson from the school of hard knocks.

I grabbed my .22 revolver and went to the gym. I put the pistol in my front pocket and walked on the basketball court. They were running a half-court game when I stood in the middle of the court and took the ball when it bounced off the rim. "Let me get the ball" someone spoke to me. "Tell that nigga to get off the court" I said while pointing at Red. "Watch out. Let me get the ball" someone else spoke. "Tell that nigga to get off the court. I ain't going anywhere until that nigga get off the court!"

The older men on the court insisted that Red leave so they could continue playing. They didn't want to be bothered by any problems he had so they made him go. Red walked out the door I followed with Loco closely behind me. Red stood his ground against my threatening presence once we got outside the building.

I pulled the weathered .22 caliber pistol out of my pocket and clutched the small gun in my oversized right palm. Red swung at me. I dodged the punch and countered by grabbing his shirt with my left hand. My right hand reached back behind my head, my eyes locked onto his head. Like lighting striking the ground my hand swung back around connecting his cheek and jaw with the metal of my gun.

Channeling the anger in my soul, I focused all the power of my being to the arm swinging the gun. I continued to connect his face to my pistol. Red fell to the ground cowering like the bitch he was. One last smack to the face with my now heated steel I cocked the hammer back and pointed it at his head. Red got up and ran for his life. I never saw Red again but I would see Norman and Kevin, later.

Loco and I were always ready to set if off at the drop of a hat. We didn't care about much but our family, our gang. We made it a point to put 16th on the map. We needed all the other hoods to know not to fuck with us. We also needed to know where everyone's hearts were at when it came to getting down out here in the streets. After I'd put down a few demonstrations that summer I was never again asked if I was scared. They knew I was down for the cause, I'd proven myself. Loco had proven himself and we were looking for them to prove themselves. Everyone we fucked with would eventually have an opportunity to show where their nuts were. I learned how to test people early. Loco and I thrived off making niggas show and prove.

The G was a free zone. We did whatever we felt like, when we felt like it. On a typical day we'd go to Colman's Liquor Store off 21st Ave. and get a 40 oz. to share. We were all under age but they'd sell us liquor. We'd go to the court and hoop all day. Taking breaks to smoke a blunt or drink.

Some days we'd line up the beer bottles that had accumulated by the basketball court and shoot at them for target practice. We'd be up there for hours shooting .22's, .9's, .38's, .40 calibers and 12 gages. We'd get tired and put the guns in the car and start back hooping. No one ever called the police or at least they never pulled up on us. We did what we wanted.

Somebody got some spray paint and I decided we need to tag the side of the school gym with our hood. That's what I did. While people were playing basketball I outlined an elaborate insignia of my name. It was cocaine white against the red brick canvas. 4 feet up and down and 10 feet across I signed the wall in Old English lettering "DASISM" and under that read "R.I.P. RALPH". I took my time to add my niggas name to the wall, much smaller than mine, one by one. "June, Playboy, Loco, Poo, 16th and Alls Well" adorned the wall, windows and door. I stepped back to look at my masterpiece. It was perfect. This was ours!

We'd mob the hood like thugs looking for trouble. We were cool with who we were cool with and everybody else could get it. Walking through the field one day with Playboy I saw Norman and Kevin. I yelled out "Let me holla at cha! Slow up. Let me holla at cha!" Playboy and I started a slow jog trying to catch up to the two of them. They started running and yelling. "We cool. You got it D. We wasn't going to jump you!" They ran away, they were scared. I never had another problem out of them again. Years later Norman got killed.

I'd seen more and done more in one summer than most people had done in a lifetime. I'd sold dope, bust guns, got some pussy, and lived as I wanted. I knew this was not what I was meant to do so I made my mind up that night that I would move back to Nap to be with my mother so I wouldn't die in the streets of the G. I left the G at the end of the summer and went back to Nap with a newfound hustle and grind.

Fall 96- Indy Balling

I went back to Nap at the end of the summer of 1996. My mother had redecorated the entire apartment with new furniture. There was a flower-patterned couch with a pull out bed in the living room with a matching love seat. The TV was a lot larger than the 19 inch we'd been crowded around before. She bought a brass and glass coffee table with matching end tables. I walked into my room to find a solid oak dresser and Chester drawers. There were new appliances in the kitchen and plaques on the walls. The apartment seemed bright and gleaming of new. I felt empowered with pride and accomplishment even though I hadn't gotten these things I knew my mother was finally getting her piece of the pie. She never asked me about my month and a half away in the G for the summer and if she did I'm sure I lied.

I had a knack for finding the people I needed when I needed them. I was hungry for the grind and shine. I spent a lot of time at the age of 16 watching people and their actions because I had nothing else to do while in Nap. I would sit for hours on the steps of my apartment watching people going in and out of their homes. I was out when there were no others outside. They had better things going on in their life and I was on the outside looking to win. The apartment kitty corner from my own had a group of older guys who hung out daily. They were in their 30's to 40's and they always had beer and I could smell the weed they would smoke in joints. The traffic was consistent with a spot but there were a lot of bitches coming in and out of the apartment. One day I gathered up enough nuts to go over to the group of men and ask "What y'all be doing out here". One of the men looked at me and said "Minding my own business" and they went back to talking like I wasn't standing there. After an awkward amount of time of me not being acknowledged I walked back to the steps in front of my apartment and sat back down to ponder my mistake. I quickly realized that I shouldn't have come to grown men like I knew them for years. I knew they were selling dope or weed over there and I wanted in, by any means necessary.

I thought about how I could approach the men again without being shut down like a kid. At the age of 16 I had a stature of a man. I waited until there was only one guy outside and I approached him for a cigarette. He gave me a square and we started talking. The guy's name was Pops and he was overweight and balding. He had grey hair horseshoed around his head. His salt and pepper undercoat of hair pillowed under the wife beater. He sat in an old vinyl lawn chair smoking a pipe. We talked about me being from the G and he told me he had people out that way. I asked him if he knew where I could get some weed. He told me his nephew would turn me on when he got back but he doesn't mess with it himself.

Pops and I learned each other's mind set as the months passed. He would let me come to his home to drink and smoke my weed while shooting the shit. I learned he was a hustler himself and they were selling dope. Pops was selling $20 rocks for the size of what I would have sold in the G for $5. Not only were the rocks small but they were blowing the dope up with b-12 to fluff it up but that took out the potency. In the G we used straight baking soda. We called it that A-1 yolla. That yolla was dense and heavy while that b-12 was light with lots of air bubbles. It really didn't matter because I knew once Pops showed me what's up he'd give me a pack to push. The mentality of an older hustler is to pray upon the hunger and bright eyes of wannabe younger pushers. They will get you high and drunk and fill your head with stories of balling out of control. They will entice you with the money, cars, clothes, women, and power to bring you in the trap. I was as wide eyed as they come. I was doing what I wanted. I was getting old heads to get me liquor and drive me around.

Pops gave me a pack and I started pushing in Aspen Village.

One of Pops soldiers was a big dude named Fat Cat. Fat Cat was the kind of nigga that had been balling his whole life and it didn't matter what he had because he knew the game has peaks and valleys. Cat would buy a pound of weed to smoke, dig in the bag, throw it on the hood of the car and tell niggas to roll up. I don't know why but Cat liked me and took me under his wing to show me the game. Cat was about 350 pounds with an s-curl faded on the sides. He drove a siliver Cutlass with chrome Dayton wires on vogue tires. He would come and pick me up from Pops spot and show me around the hoods in Nap. We would go to folks and Blood sets. Cat was good and since I was with him I was good too. I became a student of the game early and Cat taught me a lesson in making money. That red and blue gangbanging shit stops the money flow. Cat was selling to all real niggas with green money. I felt safe with Cat and I had his back.

I had become a fixture at Pops spot by September because I was making money for him and myself. I'd been telling my niggas back home about how they was raping the geekers out here with them little ass bags and bad dope. My dude convinced me to come back to the G and get some dope on a front and sell it in Nap. I did and oh boy! I tried to sell one of his and one of mine to keep Pops money flowing.

Before I knew it they only wanted the yellow dope, that yolla. I knew I wouldn't be able to sell my dope out of his house for long without him knowing so after that first rush I stopped going back to his house on a daily. I stopped copping from him and he started seeing his geekers always coming to talk to me. I was able to sell my dope until October and then things changed.

The sun was shining and it was rather warm for the time of the year. I was dressed in a red sweatshirt; black jeans with a red hat broke deep to the left. It was business as usual. I was talking to a geeker who'd sold me a watch for some dope and he wanted the watch back. He pleaded and begged to get the watch back so his wife wouldn't be mad. I told him that he could pay me twice as much as what I paid.

An old school box Chevy Caprice pulled in the parking lot. The car held three men. As they went around the curve one of the men hollered out "Almighty". I had never been shown love in Nap. Hell, I'd never even seen another Vice Lord in Nap. So as an automatic response I flagged the 5 and hollered back "Almighty". I was full of almighty, Vice Lord, pride when the car came back around the lot with another car trailing closely behind it. The two cars stopped and six men got out of the two cars. One of the men hollered out "Almighty Killer". My heart sank deep within my stomach and out my ass. I looked around to find I was alone.

I went into panic mode and dug in my pocket to grab the .22 revolver that I kept at all times and pointed it at the crowd of men. I asked the group, "What the fuck you think you gonna do now? Jump me?" I waved the gun and pointed it at all of them as I fanned it left to right. My stance was strong and my voice barked. Then one of the large men spoke up and said some of the realist shit I have ever heard to this day. "If you shoot me with that little ass pistol, one of my niggas gonna shoot you!" I thought, dam, he right. I don't even have enough bullets for all of them. Hell, one of them big niggas could take the whole chamber of these small caliber .22 bullets. I found my nuts and pointed the gun at the loud mouth and said "Fuck y'all, you ain't gonna do shit" as I backed up into the cut between the apartments. They didn't move.

I found the opening, turned my back and ran to the nearest familiar apartment door. I knocked for dear life. No one answered. I ran to the next home of a person I thought was a friend. I banged on the door. A man opened the door. I asked if I could come in because I was being chased by men. The man told me not to bring trouble to his house and closed the door. I was panicked and in fear for my life. I had nowhere to go. I decided to return to the back of my apartment to contemplate my next move.

I went to the air conditioning unit behind my apartment and I sat on it to think. I wanted to go in the house but they might still be in front. I could climb on the balcony and break the glass door. My aunt lives a few miles down the street but I don't know these niggas and they could catch me if I walk that far. What if I try another friend's house? I took the pistol out of my pocket and sat it next to me on the grid of the air conditioning unit.

I looked to my left and saw the 7-foot gate that separated me from the street. I looked ahead to see a line of apartments. I began to sink my head in utter defeat when out the corner of my eye to the right I saw a guy with braids on a grey BMX bike. I paid the biker no attention until he stopped and threw the bike down. He had a stone-cold face when he said "Ain't you that nigga that upped that pistol" while pulling a gun out his pants and shooting at me in one fluid motion. He stood in the only path out so I ran towards the gate as a retreat to safety. I touched the gate with my left hand. I had every intention to grab the top, put one foot on the gate and vault myself over. What actually happened was like out of a movie. When I touched the gate, everything slowed down. I fell to the ground and I saw streaks of dirt pop up from the ground and fall back down a grain at a time. I heard the wiz of bullets whistle past my ears then smack as they hit the apartment and cling as they hit the gate. I was down on my face. The shooting stopped.

I pressed the ground with both palms flat as if I were doing a pushup. It was eerily quiet as I lifted my head to see if my assailant was standing overhead to finish what he started. Slowly I veered around me to find no one. The man and the bike were gone. I stood up, patted my body from neck to feet to confirm I hadn't been shot. I touched every part of my body fearing I'd find a hole in my body and blood coming from a place where once I was whole. I picked up my pistol and dug in my pocket to find I still possessed my pack. I was ok and untouched. My heart beat relaxed and my fear turned to anger. Someone would pay for what they just did.

I gathered myself physically and emotionally and went to Pops house. Pops opened the door after several knocks. He invited me in and asked if that was me getting shot at a few minutes ago. My body and mind told me to put all five shots in his head when he turned his back but I could not prove he set me up and there were other people in the house.

I sat down and gave him the low down on what just went on outside. He rolled a joint and passed me a beer. Pops told me that I needed to watch who I crossed. His story broke down to the fact that I was young and new around. He told me I was disrespectful wearing my hat like I did around gangsters and it was bound to happen. Pops talked to me for the next six hours.

The fact of it was I was scared to leave and go home. Soon I was drunk and high to the point of stumbling and I finally felt at ease. I left his house and walked the 20 paces to my apartment. I fell up the stairs and entered my apartment.

I stayed in that apartment for 2 weeks straight. I was above my head in this gangster shit and I knew it. I underestimated all the Gangster's since the day I moved to Nap. I didn't care how many of them there would be if I had a gun on me I would walk through sets with my red on and hat broke to the left. I was from murder capitol city who was gonna fuck with me?

I now knew there are real thug niggas in every city. I'd crossed the wrong nigga and while I sat in my room day and night I could look out my window to see business as usual at Pops spot. Who could I blame?

I wanted to make money too. I knew I couldn't go back to Pops spot but how can I be stuck in here while they get paid. My mind began to formulate plans to take Pops spot down. To be honest the first thing that I thought of was to call the police to have his shit raided. I pondered that long and hard for a few days. I imagined sitting in the window while the drug unit kicked in his shit. I envisioned him getting drug out in that fucking tight ass wife beater in the dead cold of the night while I watched, laughed and smoked a blunt. I couldn't do that to a nigga as much as I wanted him to feel like I did. I could never call the police on a person. Signing my own death certificate was a fascination of mine. What I would have to do would prove my point for good.

I became accustom to watching people and their movement in my time alone. The key to watching people is you also recognize their patterns and schedules. I could pinpoint within a 15-minute window when everyone in my building would go to or come home from work. I could do the same for Pops building. I knew cars, boyfriends, girlfriends, family members and drug deals. I could see it all from my window and unconsciously I had memorized everything and everyone. Like clockwork Pop's worker would pull his pea green big body Pontiac in the parking space under my window at 6 in the morning. He would go to Pops house, go inside for about ten to fifteen minutes and come back out and walk to the gas station four blocks up the street. He would come back with a coffee and usually smoking a square. He'd get back in his car and drive around the complex a few times then leave. He'd come back at 11 in the afternoon and stay until it got dark while going in and out of Pops spot. Sometimes you do what your heart tells you is right. I'm a man of principal and I hadn't forgotten that I was setup. This guy would always have a weird vibe when I was around him. He was over Pops house as much as me when I was bumping. I remember he'd had some of his friends come through and they were looking at me funny one day. As I sat in my personal solitary confinement I'd come to the conclusion that Pops set me up and he was the worker who put it all together. I know he had something to do with it.

I awoke to my mother leaving out the house as she did daily before the sun rose at 5 am. She had to catch the bus downtown and transfer from there to catch the Castleton bus so she had to leave early. I never had to go to school because she trusted I was doing what I was supposed to do but I wasn't, not even close.

Moms had no clue I hadn't been out they house in 2 weeks. I had everything I needed there. I waited for Mr. 6 am to pull his green Pontiac in the space under my window. Like clockwork he did. When he got out the car to walk across the lot to Pops spot my hand was already on my door knob to leave out.

I was wearing my black jeans, black hoodie, black hat and black sneakers. In my left pocket were my house key and my 6 inch hunter's knife. In my right pocket I griped my pistol which I freshly oiled. Before he entered Pops spot I was at the bottom of the steps. My leg was shaky. I could see my breath blowing out of my mouth like smoke because of the early morning frost. I almost went back inside when I thought to myself now or never. I walked up to the Pontiac, pulled out my knife and poked a whole in the sidewall of the tire and slipped the knife around. I repeated the same thing for each tire until they were all flat.

I ran up the street to the other end of the complex. A gate ran along the street for about a block until it ran out. There was a whole in the gate that was put there by someone who didn't want to walk all the way around to leave out the complex. My body stretched through the gate until I was free. I walked up the street and sat on the steps of the church. Within 10 minutes I saw my victim walk pass me as I knew he would on his way to get his coffee. He paid me no attention as the steps of the church were off the street and pushed back. He knew not what I planned for him.

I watched as he entered the gas station. When he came back out I had position myself on the corner. I knew he'd walk pass me. The sun began to peak over the horizon. I'd run this scenario in my head a thousand times and I was going to do it. He was a block away. My heart began racing.

I squeezed the pistol in my pocket tight. I began to sweat under my hat and I had to take my hand out of my pocket to whip my forehead. When I put my hand back in my pocket it was cold. He was on my block now and coming closer. I clutched the pistol and with my thumb I pulled the hammer back in my pocket. My head was down as I leaned on the metallic utility box painted yellow that was on the corner.

He was in ear range and before I looked up at him I asked him for a square. He began patting his pockets and dug in his left coat pocket. I pulled out my pistol. Pressed it to his stomach and pulled the trigger 2 times. Unlike when I got shot at and everything slowed down, this happen very quickly.

He let out several gut-wrenching grunts while he grabbed his stomach. Before he fell to his knees I was running around the corner. I went the back way into the complex through the hole in the gate. I ran around several of the buildings and came in behind my building.

I went back up the stairs into my apartment. I got in the shower as soon as I got in the house, changed clothes and was looking out my window within 15 minutes of the shooting. I watched and waited to see an ambulance or police cars. It was a half an hour before the police blocked off the street and an ambulance came.

I embraced the moment. My nervousness increased at every foot step I heard coming up the steps outside. Every knock on a neighbor's door and door slam jolted through my body. I stayed fixed to the window in anticipation of the police coming to get me. I was nervous wreck.

When my mother came home that night I could not withhold the emotions inside of me. She looked at my face and knew something was wrong. What's the matter she asked? Tears began streaming down my face. I wept like a child. I started breathing hard and I buried my face into my mother's warm embrace. She held me and told me whatever it was we'd work it out. I told my mother everything that had happened within the last two weeks.

She listened as I talked and we rocked together. When I'd calm down and told my story she looked at me and said don't worry we won't stay here. I knew then my moms would do anything in her power to keep me safe. She broke the lease and got a transfer from her job in Castleton paying well and got to move to MC. I was taken to my aunt's house and in three days we were in Michigan City (MC).

Winter 96- Michigan City

The last 9 months of my life I'd grown and seen more than I'd seen or done in the last 15 years. I was learning about myself and my capabilities. I was no longer a member of a gang. I was a beast on my own. When I got to MC it was the end of October. We moved into a nice apartment complex named Normandy Village. MC was small but only about 30 minutes away from the G. MC was known for the $1 movie theater, beach, and outlet shopping mall.

MC had one high school so everyone knew everyone. They'd grown up together from elementary in the same cohort. I quickly noticed the glances and stares as I was given a tour of the high school on the day I registered. I heard kids in the classes asking each other if they knew who that was. I could hear them whisper "He tall".

I had grown a few inches and towered over the teachers with my 6′8″ frame. My afro was plush and thick. I used the hairdryer to blow it out on a Bone Thugs and Harmony status. I was wearing the latest gear and had the stroll of a baller. I was excited to come into a city that was small.

I was excited to have a fresh start. No one knows me here and with what I know I can be somebody in this city. I was given a locker and schedule of classes I was to attend. I actually had study hall. I'd only heard about that on TV in a school full of white people. I knew this would be different. I would play the background and see how they flowed. I was gangsta but wise enough to know I had to get in where I fit in. I had to see who was who and who ran what. High school was a breeding ground for baby gangsters and ballers who had family ties and connections. I knew how to look for what I needed, instinctively.

I spent the night pressing my outfit for my first day at the new school. I awoke early to go to the bus stop. I wanted to be there before the other kids got there so I wouldn't feel awkward. I would have an easier time starting a conversation if I could be there first. I needed to be comfortable and control how I was perceived. As I'd planned the kids started coming up one at a time to the bus stop.

The first person I met was a stocky guy named Booty. Booty had a full beard and a wino belly. He extended his sweaty sausage like fingers to shake my hand. I shook his hand like a man. He tried to end the shake with the forks up. He was folks. I looked him in his eye and told him "I ain't folks", then snatched my hand away.

We started talking and to my surprise he asked me if my name was D. I told him "yes". He asked if I was a Vice Lord from Gary. I said "yes". This conversation fucked me up because he knew me and my whereabouts.

I hadn't even gotten the chance to say anything about myself and Booty was calling me out. If this was how it was going down on the first day, so be it. The next question out his mouth threw me. He asked if I was Latina's boyfriend. I said "who". He said yeah you're Latina's boyfriend.

Hell, maybe I was Latina's boyfriend. I asked Booty "who is Latina"? He explained that Latina was a big titty Mexican with long hair. I told him I had no idea who that was. He asked me if I was 6"8′ and I said "yes". He restated, yeah you are Latina's boyfriend. He then went to explain that "Dasism from the G" was dating Latina. "A few months back you went to jail for carjacking a man at the McDonald's. You stole her daddy's gun, went to the McDonald's and jacked a nigga." I told him it wasn't me. My mind began to race with thoughts. The bus pulled up and I got on.

Our bus stop was the last pickup on the route. We could see the school from our apartment. We were literally down the street maybe a mile or so. Michigan City was built in the middle of farm land and there were no sidewalks to use in most of the city. The road was a two-lane street so narrow that cars could barely pass each other. Corn stalks running parallel to the road cast shadows on cars. Every school bus going to the school would rumble by as we stood there. Every kid in the city driving to school passed us up as we stood.

Finally, our bus appeared, slowed down, breaks squeaking, and stopped. The white light strobed on top of the bus as the stop sign popped out the side signaling others to stop. I was the last person to enter the crowded, already full bus. Everyone glared with amazement as I crouched down the aisle attempting to locate an empty seat. The bus was dank with moisture, bad breath, and teenage funk.

I was a presence standing over 6 feet tall with an afro another foot. Finding an empty was no option so I sat in the front, behind the driver. The bus ride was all of 2 minutes to school.

All of the buses lined up in front of the all brick building and we just sat there until it was time to go inside the school. The bell rang and all the lined-up busses opened the doors and released a flood of kids pouring into the parking lot. Everyone piled through the parking lot and funneled through the doors of the school.

I was trying to see all the girls while I walked but the momentum from the flow of the crowd pushed me faster than I would have liked to go. Hugs were being given to friends not seen since the prior week. The administration spent their morning breaking those displays of affection and sending students on their way.

I absorbed memories of the first time I'd saw a glass wall cubing the entire library that sat in the middle of the school. I got to my locker and I felt energy from the newness of my experience.

People were walking pass me talking in groups. Sounds were muffled in a low roar as conversations mixed. Glares were shot my way as I stood against my locker watching, observing and listening. I heard it over and over, "that's Dasism from the G". Did my reputation precede me, I thought? Who was this carjacker from the G that everyone thinks I am?

In the majority of my morning classes' the students were white but there were enough blacks to make me feel comfortable. I was given an assigned seat in every class and I obliged to sit where told. I was in full, I don't give a fuck mode when I walked into each class.

I was the new kid coming in the middle of the school year I had to leave a first impression on all the niggas and bitches in every class that I wasn't the one to fuck with. I'd realized that since there was only one high school in the whole city word would spread like wild fire of my swagger. They already thought I was someone I wasn't. I played my part.

Lunch hour came and I'd told myself I wouldn't be the outcast at lunch like I was in Nap. I got in one of the multiple lines of the food carts. The carts sat three on each side of the lunch room selling specialty foods such as popcorn, corn dogs, ice cream or nachos. The main lunch line snaked to the front of the lunch room. The center of the massive space sat a cluster of blue bench like tables. I was invited to a table by a caramel skinned girl. I sat and she introduced me to everyone at the table. The conversation was flowing and I felt good and welcomed.

After the lunch period was over I went back to my locker and was approached by a 5 foot mocha covered girl named Daga. Daga had a head full of black and brown braids draping over her shoulders and down her back. She was pulling a Mexican female over to me. She introduced herself and then introduced the Mexican girl as Latina. Latina was a pale skinned Mexican with natural blushed cheeks. She stood about a foot shorter than me. Her hair was naturally brown and fully curled down her back in tight spirals. Her soft brown eyes gave me a view clear to her soul as they twinkled when she looked up at me. Latina had large breasts and skin that looked as delicate as a porcelain doll. Latina looked me in my face and said, "you're not my D from the G"!

She looked relived. I on the other hand felt a massive thump in my chest. I was the new guy and if I had to blast off on a sexy female, so be it. I was not going to let anyone think I am taking any shit from anyone. She explained that she had been hearing rumors all day that her ex-boyfriend was going to the school and everyone thought I was he. She told me that he was 6"8′ and he was a Vice Lord from Gary. She asked me to meet her after school to walk to the bus. I agreed.

Our walk to the bus afterschool was full of questions about the G and who I knew, where I went to school and what part of town I hung around. We exchanged phone numbers and parted ways. Latina and I became fast friends as our walk to the bus after school became a ritual. Latina was a happy person full of joy and cheer. She would make my day with the smile on her face or the glint in her eye.

We'd talk on the phone for hours after school talking about nothing and everything at the same time. There was never a dull moment in our conversation. I was a good listener and she could talk. Latina had a boyfriend living in the state of Michigan. Latina would get one of her friends to drive her out of state to see him when she could.

Latina would tell me about how she would go all out for him but he did not appreciate her efforts. I was at a point in my life where I tried not to hate on the next man for my own benefit and as much as I would have liked to, I couldn't.

Latina was the kind of girl who had a job and worked for what she wanted at an early age. When she was feeling how a nigga was acting towards her she would buy her man gifts to show here appreciation. She'd tell me stories of how she gave him money and generally looked out for his needs. I never had a girl do things like that for me. My nature is shy towards females but if I had a girl like her I would show her I was feeling that kind of treatment. We talked often but we were in a friend zone.

I made friends quickly in MC. One of the guys on the school bus stops name was KD. KD was a track star and football player, a jock. KD was about 6 feet 2 inches and a solid 160. I met KD in the summer of our 11th grade year. He rarely caught the bus during the school year but I was seeing him around the complex. I hung around the apartment complex during my free time because I didn't have much to do in the summer. I would walk around and get a good feel for my surroundings.

I had access to go to the G when I wanted. I would catch the train when my money was right to go to the G and get a quarter pound (QP) of weed from my man. During my first few months at the school I found out a lot kids looking for good weed but couldn't get access. I saw my opportunity to get in where I fit. Everyone who got on at my bus stop smoked weed. Booty turned me on to his clique and from there word of mouth spread that Dasism had that good bud. I was selling about a QP a week in dimes and quarters. Most of the people I fucked with had my beeper number.

Summer 97

In the summer, I would post up at the pool and look at the grown women in bathing suits. White women with blonde hair and tan lines. Hispanic women with perfectly tanned skin and long wavy hair. Black women with the bodies of goddesses. They all inspired me to spend long hours at the pool. One afternoon I saw KD at the pool and we began chopping it up. We got cool quick because KD was from the G. He had lived in MC for most of his life but still had family in the G. Through our conversations I learned that his aunt did hair and she gave my brother a Jeri Curl back in the day when she was dating my uncle. I liked KD because he knew all the fine girls at school and they knew him. I wanted to learn from him and become a jock.

When I went to his house there was always a football game on the TV. I never understood how someone could watch ESPN all day long. We would go over to his friend's house and it would be the same thing, football and ESPN. I was used to watching Jerry Springer, the Basement on BET, TRL on MTV, and playing video games. I told myself I would learn. KD saw how I was making money and wanted to know how he could get down to make some money too. I told him that he didn't want to hustle because he had too much going for him. I asked him if he ever smoked weed before and he told me "no".

I introduced KD to smoking weed the same summer. It was the first time I saw someone get high for the first time. It was funny. KD's moms worked midnights, and had friends she would hang out with, so he would have the house to himself a lot of the time.

One afternoon, his mother was gone, we sat in his living room and I rolled up a blunt. He was inexperienced to smoking so I had to school him. I told him to hold the blunt between his pointer finger and his thumb, puff on the blunt and suck the smoke down his throat. He held the blunt and looked at it for a second or two. He placed it to his lips and took the smallest puff I'd ever seen.

KD started coughing and choking. He turned bright red by the end of his convulsion. KD had light brown eyes that turned blood shot red and glossy in seconds. His usual bright-eyed look faded away to reveal eyes so low it looked as if he was sleeping. KD didn't want to hit the blunt again. He let me finish the rest in the apartment as he sat in a daze. I finished the blunt and flushed the ashes we'd been dumping in the inside of a CD case down the toilet. I left his house. The evening had darkened the landscape of the rolling hills of Normandy Village as I returned home, walking and high.

The next day I called KD to make sure he was cool. He told me he'd been knocked out since I left and had just awaked when my phone call rang him out of his sleep. KD said he like how he felt and wanted to try it again. I told him no doubt! The next time, I told him, we would smoke outside so he wouldn't want to go to sleep. KD and I spent the rest of the summer smoking and kicking it around the complex. I turned him on to all the old heads who were too old to gang bang but had that banging mentality. Most of the old heads were on the run from something they did in the G and had to move away from imminent death. Some of them moved to MC to hustle crack and powder. MC was the perfect spot to take over if you had superior product. I was just like them. I'd moved here to get away from what happened in Nap.

I was trying to make a name for myself as the weed man so keeping it was a priority. I was befriended by a guy named Pocahontas. Pocahontas was in his early twenties and from the G. He was one of those light skinned pretty boys with long hair down his back. Pocahontas drove a pearl colored Lincoln Mark VIII. We clicked because of our work ethics. Pocahontas was a real baller. He was bringing 2 to 3 ounces of crack a week to MC from the G. I didn't know that when we met.

I was introduced to Pocahontas through a guy about my height but he had me in weight by about 100 lbs., named Wood. Wood was a part time hustler. He was the type of hustler that didn't have a lot of cliental but kept work in case someone was looking. Wood was a well-known entity in MC but stayed under the radar.

Wood and Pocahontas were running together when I came on the scene. Wood and I got cool and if there was a need for weed I got the call. That's how I was introduced to Pocahontas, by selling him some killer. I networked all summer long. I stayed visible so anyone who was out and about as I was got to know me.

All summer long I hung out in Normandy Village, smoking, drinking and politicking. I met all the players of the game who resided in the complex. By the time the summer was over I was moving about a half a pound a week in quarters, half ounces and ounces. I had a network of hustlers and thugs who respected my gangster and allowed me to be down. I was the youngest in the clique and getting more seasoned by the day. I was introduced to older hoes that were down for anything if you smoked a blunt or gave the illusion that you were a shot caller. MC empowered my thirst for money and hoes.

Peer Pressure

School started back and I was getting rides by KD's friend, a white boy named Brad. Brad was the typical wigger, not to knock his swag, but he wanted to be down so bad it was funny to me. Brad would let KD drive his car during the day in case he got some pussy or just wanted to dip out. I persuaded KD to get the car one day because I wanted to get a tattoo. Neither KD nor I had a driver's license. I told KD we needed to go to the G because they won't ask for ID.

After some peer pressure and a blunt or two we were on interstate 80/94 west going to the G. I told him to get off on Broadway and go south to Roy Boy's tattoo shop. KD and I were both big for our age and looked like grown men. I told the tattoo guy what I wanted done and he sketched it out. I signed off on a waiver for the ink.

I sat in the tattoo chair and took a deep breath. KD stood next to me watching the artist. The sketch was transferred onto a carbon copy type of paper. That paper was then placed on my arm and angled so it was straight. He wet the paper and the picture he drew, transferred and was stenciled on my arm.

He used the outline of the copy to begin his work. The buzz from the tattoo gun sounded like a high-powered pair of hair cutting liners. He placed the needle in my arm and I jumped. He told me to be still unless I wanted a bad tat. My heart raced as he tore through my skin. It felt like a knife cutting me with precision. I gathered myself and zoned out. After a few minutes, the pain had numbed and I was able to handle it without grimacing. All I could think about was how I was doing this for my brother. He'd never be forgotten and this tat will be forever. My brother will be on my side until the day I leave this earth.

I was tattered with a TuPac cross in memory of my brother it said, "RIP Ralph 77/96". The cross was black and grey with a ribbon that snaked in and out 3 times from top to bottom. In the background behind the cross was a red rose with a green stem. After the artist completed his work he looked me in the eye and slapped my fresh new tat. The numbness in my arm that I had become accustom to began throbbing after the unsuspected slap. I looked at it in the mirror and a sense of pride and accomplishment overwhelmed my soul. I rolled a blunt and we smoked on the way home. I was excited and kept telling KD "I told you I could do it". I couldn't wait for the day to show off my new tat. We made it back to school before the end of the school day and we were sitting in the parking lot when Brad walked out.

This was my junior year of school and I had already made a name for myself and I'd planned on being the hardest thug in the school. I was in a city where everybody was folks. It didn't make a difference to me because I was Vice Lord to the core. I wanted someone to try me. I had my .22 revolver and I was fucking with real thugs in my apartment complex. School shit was nothing. One-day KD and I skipped school and went to a skip party at this white girl's house named PJ.

PJ was a thick girl and at that time in my life I'd never really been attracted to white girls. We smoked a few blunts and drank some beer in the basement of her house. A little guy, who was trying to get down with us, named Petty came with us that day. Petty was about 5 feet tall and kept weed. He must have had a gangster daddy because he stayed in name brand clothing and he wore gold rings, a thick gold rope, and a gold dope boy herringbone. Petty's bone was at least an inch thick, it was nice.

We smoked a few blunts and Petty got comfortable and took off his gold. He laid it on the bed all nice and neat. It was almost weird how he lined the chains up perfectly parallel to each other, straightening out any bends to create perfect lines of gold. KD and PJ were kissing and feeling on each other. It got hot and heavy so they went upstairs and left Petty and me in the basement.

Petty and I snuck upstairs because we could hear PJ moaning. They were in the middle of the living room floor on top of a blanket laid on the ground. PJ was on her back with her legs in the air and KD was on top of her. He had her legs in a lock with his arms ensuring to keep them up in the air. PJ moaned louder as KD stroked her hard and fast. For the first time in my life I saw a naked white girl and I liked what I saw. They switched positions and PJ got on all fours and let KD enter her from behind. I saw her nipples were pink and her body was smooth. I wanted to fuck her too.

I went back down stairs before Petty and his gold immediately caught my eye. I took the dope boy herringbone, went to the bathroom and stuffed it in my draws. Petty came back down stairs and laid on the bed and went to sleep. After a few hours, it was time to go. We were all in the room when KD woke up Petty. Petty started putting on his jewelry and noticed right off that his bone was gone. They were all surprised and the search began. We looked under the bed, in the hall, the bathroom and everywhere else we could think of. Petty figured one of us had it and began accusing us. I was the first to flip out my pockets, pull up my pants legs and remove my shoes to prove I didn't have his bone. We searched for an hour. Petty kept saying "that's my dad's bone, stop playing". I would search harder every time his frustration flared. KD finally said we got to go because school was about to get out and we needed to pick up Brad. Petty protested as we walked out and got in the car.

As soon as we got in the car KD asked "did you take it". I told him to pull off so we could get Brad in time. At the first stop light he asked again, "did you take it". I paused and took a deep breath. "I won't tell him if you did", he said trying to relieve any of my apprehensions. I took another deep breath and looked him in the eye. I unzipped my coat, took off my seat belt, and I pulled the bone out of my draws. We laughed all the way back to school.

I was smart enough to never wear the bone to school. I shined it up every day in anticipation to wear it soon. One Friday night KD and I went to the bowling alley. I figured it had been months since I took the chain and I'd be good. I pressed a fly outfit and cleaned my shoes. We walked to the bowling alley which was directly behind the complex.

As soon as we walked in the bowling alley the magnificence of the bone caught the light and glittered around my neck as it should. 10 steps in, Shannon looked up and I could hear him say "that's Petty's bone", to his guy. All night I was getting compliments on the necklace. I knew that I would have to get rid of the bone before it got back to Petty that I was wearing his chain. I was never worried about Petty but he used to kick it with us and to think your friend got you is not the gangsta I was trying to portray. I wasn't his friend though.

I learned early in life that there were weak and strong people. The smart and strong can and will exploit that weakness. I wore the bone in public in MC one time only. I went to the G the next week and sold the bone to Loco for $250. Loco had the bone for years and every time I would see it I would think I should have kept it. I sold it too cheap.

As my junior year of high school progressed Latina and I got closer. Latina and I talked on the phone almost every day. I walked her to the bus every day after school. We were just cool since she had a boyfriend in Michigan. I was digging her personality and loyalty to her dude. I didn't want a girlfriend at school. I was introduced to a senior named Chris. I can't remember how but Chris and I got cool quick. Chris had a brown Monte Carlo and she was the type of girl that was a pleaser. She liked my thug ways and the fact I was from the G. I could call Chris and ask her to take me to the G and she was always down for a road trip. I was not interested in Chris at the time. I was just happy to be able to get back and forth to the G without worrying about how the busses and trains ran. Chris was happy with being a part of the gangster shit we were living.

We would go to the G, get some killa and hang out in the hood. She would watch us play basketball and talk shit. My dude Bro was feeling Chris so I would let him take her on tours of the hood while I chilled. Bro would take her behind the school right off the basketball court and fuck the shit out of her almost every time she brought me. That was the routine for months. Go to the G, I'd kick it, she'd get with Bro and they'd fuck. One afternoon I was shitty when we got to the G.

Chris, Loco and I were in her ride smoking a blunt. Loco got to telling me about them niggas who killed my brother and the fact that they were still around. He and I came up with the plan to drive down on the End and kill a nigga. The End was a five-square block radius from Virginia St to Broadway going east and west and from 15th Ave to 20th Ave going north and south.

The End was the Mecca of crack fiends that we called geekers. There were more dope spots in one concentrated area than around the whole city and that was what we called the End. Loco was telling me that one of the guys named Twan had a spot on the End and we could get him. I always had my .22 with me when I went to the G. I told Chris to take us to the End to find Twan. Two blocks in to the End I saw Twan walking down the street. I told Chris to bend a block, drive pass him and stop. She complied fully. We stopped and I told Chris to call his name.

I figured that this nigga would reply because Chris was a cute girl and she was driving. She called his name as I sat in the passenger seat trying to be low. Twan turned around and started walking toward the car. Twan got to the back of the car. I reached around Chris and unloaded the revolver in Twan's direction.

The revolver sounded like a loud pack of firecrackers but was loud enough to put fire under Twan's ass. Twan slipped and with one motion got up and ran for his life. The bottom of his shoes and his elbows swinging in the air got smaller as he fled in the distance. Chris had a tight grip on the steering wheel and a look like the life had just been sucked out of her face, stunned. I calmly told Chris "drive".

She pulled off and was headed straight back to the hood. I told her not to go to the hood, instead take me to the cemetery where my brother was buried. Loco was in the back seat rolling up a blunt. Music blared as we were all amped from the demonstration we just did. The trip to the cemetery seemed quick.

Loco fired up the blunt as we pulled up to the area where he was laid for his eternal sleep. We got out the car and stood at my brother's head stone. The grass was slightly overgrown so I began pulling the grass that was covering the edges of his head stone. I peered upon the writing on Ralph's head stone and took a deep breath of the marijuana smoke.

His headstone was black and bronze. It had an angel in the corner of it peering into the heavens. I told myself as I stood there that I would avenge my brother's death. I would hunt down everyone who had something to do with my brother being killed. I would hunt down anyone who was affiliated with someone who had something to do with his death. No one was safe, including me. Chris kept telling me that "this some real shit, I feel this shit, this shit real". She had never seen a person get shot or shot at.

When Chris and I got back to MC that night we sat on the steps of my apartment talking for hours. She started confessing about all the gangster shit she had done in her lifetime. She told me she never saw someone run like Twan. Chris started looking at me deeply and it made me feel she liked me. She began asking me about what kind of girls I was into and why I didn't have a girlfriend. In all the time she and I hung out I'd never looked at Chris like that. She was the homegirl. Out of nowhere Chris pulled her tit out and started sucking her nipple. I never wanted Chris until then. That tit turned me on instantly. I asked her to let me suck it. She put it back in the bra and went home. After witnessing that first gangsta demonstration Chris would bring me food, squares and pretty much anything I wanted. All I had to do was ask.

Chris graduated that year in June, the end of my junior year, and she had a party in my apartment complex. All the ballers of the school were there and grown women too. That night is rather blurry to me but what I remember is I came with a party pack of killa. I was rolling blunt after blunt and drinking whatever I was passed. It started off as a party full of people and loud music. Smoke layered the room as people played spades on the table and the others danced or hugged the walls talking shit. In a blink there was just Chris and I. I was sitting on the couch and I must have dosed off. When I awoke I was looking at the big screen TV in front of me showing white noise. The lights were off and I saw the slow-moving silhouette of Chris's naked body crawling across the floor. Her large tits drooped and swayed with every movement as she prowled towards her pray. She climbed on me and we began taking my clothes off. Our bodies pressed and increased the heat in the room. The next thing I know is we were making out. She smothered me with her moist warmth in the bed we'd made our way to. I began fucking the shit out of Chris. We seemed to have fucked for hours. I remember walking home, taking my clothes off and there was a foul smell in my clothes that stuck in my nose for days. Chris and I never really talked after that.

The summer before my senior year was exciting. My niggas from the hood would catch the train from time to time up to MC from the G. I always had killa on deck and I could always get someone to go get us some liquor. June and Bro came to visit me. When they got there we smoked and caught up on lost time.

Bro told me that he didn't have any money to catch the train back home. I was confused. I had money for train fare, but he shouldn't have gone out of town without any money. We came up with a plan to steal a car later that night. When my brother was alive I'd rolled around with him in stolen cars we called steamers. I'd never personally stolen a car myself nor had I seen one stolen. We kind of knew what we had to do but only in pieces.

We waited until night fall and began lurking around the parking lot of the complex. I didn't know how to break in the cars and neither did Bro or June. We would go from car to car pulling on the door handles and if the car was unlocked we tried to steal it. Normandy Village was a nice apartment complex with trusting individuals who were not used to being the pray for predators like us.

I would get in the car first while June and Bro stood as look outs in the cut holding the chopper. My role was to break the steering column so Bro could get in the car and remove the silver horse shoe looking metal piece. Once the horse shoe piece was removed a flat head screw driver could be used to pull up the switch. The switch was normally pulled up when the ignition was turned by key, under the steering column.

Once the steering column was broken it would expose the switch under the metal horseshoe. We figured out a good system after destroying about 10 cars. On the 11th car things changed.

Now that we knew how to get a steamer that's what we did. Every time they'd come to MC on the train they'd go home in a steamer. We'd gotten the routine down to a science. The last time we tried to take a car together was a close one. Night had fallen and it was pitch black in the shadows not illuminated by the street lights.

June and Bro were in the cut with the chopper. They stood in the shadows being cast by the large apartment building. I was felling the adrenaline pump through me as my heart beat increased. I opened the door of a blue short body sedan. I used a flash light to see what I was doing. I closed the door so the dome light wouldn't come on and give away my presence. I used my trusty screw driver to pry the plastic column away from its frame. I left the screw driver and the flashlight on the seat as I exited the car so Bro could get in and work his magic.

Like the changing of the guard I took the chopper from Bro as he entered the car. I pulled the hood over my head and became a part of the shadows. June stood next to me in complete silence as we watched out for anyone watching us. Bro closed the door and began working. In less than a minute of him working a man came down the steps with a bag of garbage.

I tried to signal Bro to get low but as I watched the man I could see Bro sink into the seat of the car. The man walked next the car that Bro was in and glanced in the window but he didn't turn his head. I clutched the .22 in my pocket and pulled the hammer back. I placed my finger over the trigger, removed it from my pocket, and put it at my side.

The man wore a grey sweat suit. He dumped the garbage in the dumpster and came back passed the car and looked in without turning his head. June and I didn't move as we felt the shadows concealed our outlines. Without looking back the man went back up the stairs into his apartment. Bro looked up and we waved him over to get out the car. We ran back to my apartment to laugh about almost being seen and caught.

One thing about my youth was that I would get on a one-track mind set. I wouldn't stop or move on to something else until I satisfied my craving for doing what I wanted. We sat in the apartment smoking a blunt planning our next move.

We went back outside and came upon a black 4 door Bonneville. The doors were unlocked so we welcomed ourselves. I cracked the neck and Bro came over to do his part. June and I went to the cut to watch out. Bro started the car on the first try. June and I ran up to the car, opened the doors and Bro pulled off.

Excited and scared at the same time we drove out of the complex watching for anyone who may have seen us or called the police. I directed Bro to the highway through the back-country roads with no street lights. Once on the highway I knew we were home free as long as we weren't speeding or swerving. Bro paid close attention to his driving while June and I looked through the car for valuables. We'd made it to the G. We did it and it felt good.

I spent the night at Bro's house and in the morning he took me to the train station so I could go home. I told Bro to burn the steamer or sell it before it got hot. Once a steamer was hot, every police would be looking for it. He told me he'd drive it for a few days then he was going to dump it.

After a few weeks I got a call from June. June told me that Bro still had the steamer and he was keeping it in the garage at his house. June told me Bro was washing the car and taking it up to the schools on lunch hour to fuck with the bitches. I was told that Bro and Loco went up to West Side High School and got chased by the police because they were on school grounds and the police ran the license plate and found out it was stolen.

June told me that Bro got into a high-speed chase with the police. "Bro was driving through yards and in between houses. He was doing about 100 mph down the streets. He got away though", June told me. I could only think that I know I told him to dump the damn car.

I called Bro to see what was going on. Bro told me that he did get in a high-speed chase from the police but he got away. "I aint tripping, D. Them punk as dicks ain't got nothing over here. I got this, D, don't trip. I been keeping the whip in the garage anyway", Bro told me. The next morning, I got a call from Bro. "They stole the steamer" Bro told me. "How the hell did you get the steamer stole", I said? He told me that he fell asleep and forgot to put it in the garage. When he woke up it was gone. I was happy the car was gone because I didn't want my nigga to go to jail for something like stealing a car.

The next time my nigga Bro came out to MC he came by himself. My nigga Bro was always looking for the hook up or the quick come up. He caught the train and would act like he was sleeping so when the conductor came to collect the tickets he would think Bro was already on the train from an earlier pick up. Bro would get away with shit like that all the time.

He caught the bus to my apartment. It was the middle of the summer before my senior year. I always had some killa on deck so smoking was never a problem. We went to the pool. The pool in Normandy Village was the place to be on a hot day. The sexy white women would be in their two-piece bikinis. They would get out of the water looking like a dripping wet fantasy. I would sit in the cut watching under my hat which was tipped low to cover my eyes.

Bro had the gift to gab and could strike up a conversation with anyone at any time. He talked a white boy into letting him ride his bike around the pool. Lap after lap Bro rode around the pool. A sexy white woman in a black one piece was sitting in the lawn chair smoking a square. Bro stopped and asked her for a square and she told him "no".

Bro tried to entice her but she didn't give in to his commands. Finally, Bro got fed up and started talking shit to her. He called her a bitch and white hoe before she got up and started snapping off on him. As she walked through the gate of the pool she said, "that's alright I'm a get my boyfriend to teach you how to talk to a woman" and left. I never said a word while they were passing verbal jabs at each other.

Within ten minutes the white lady was back. She came to the gate with a 6-foot 350 pound black guy and pointed at Bro. Bro was still riding the bike around the pool. "That's him" is all I heard. The guy came in the pool and asked Bro if he called his woman a bitch.

Bro continued to ride around the pool and told the guy "fuck you and your bitch". The guy told him to get off the bike and talk to him like a man. Bro continued his laps around the pool while shouting out shit like "G.I., Almighty and I ain't from this bitch".

The guy stopped the bike on his third lap pass him and told Bro to apologize to his woman. Bro got off the bike and went in on the guy. Bro looked that big 350-pound nigga in his eye and told him to get the fuck out his face.

The guy decided he didn't want the confrontation with Bro and said "I don't want to hurt your little ass but the next time you say something to my woman I'm a beat your ass". He turned his back on Bro and started walking towards the gate to leave. Bro said in his deepest most sincere gangster voice "Fuck you and that bitch, G.I.".

The guy stood at the entrance of the gate for a few seconds thinking of his next move. He turned around walked up to Bro and grabbed him in a bear hug. He picked Bro up off the ground and slammed him into the gate.

He told Bro "You little niggas need some respect. I'm a grown ass man. I ain't got time to be playing with your little ass". Against the gate and helpless Bro told the guy "Fuck you". The guy got pissed and threw Bro to the ground. He put his knee on Bro's chest and started choking him out. The white lady was on the other side of the gate yelling "let him go. You gonna kill him". People at the pool started backing away from the altercation. I was still in the cut watching the whole thing unfold.

Big dude and the white lady had no clue Bro and I was together. I couldn't let this go on any longer on my watch. Bro was losing the fight, but his mouth was running 100 miles per hour. I sprang into action without a word being said. I grabbed the long lawn chair, which allowed you to stretch your legs out, closest to where they were fighting. I swung it above my head with as much momentum as I could muster and smashed the aluminum frame on the big dudes back.

Before the chair hit the ground I was on his back giving him a 5 piece to the jaw. He rolled off of Bro in shock. I kicked him in his fat ass belly. Bro got up and we both got to yelling "Almighty". The guy got up and said "oh y'all gonna jump me. That's ok be here when I get back I'm a kill both y'all little nigga's". Bro amped up "go get them niggas, guns, whatever, fuck yall, G. I."!

The guy and his lady got back in their car and drove off. One of the girls at the pool ran up to me and told me that was Tootie and he didn't play. I told her Tootie was a bitch. She said he ran with some gangsta ass niggas and we should go. I took what she said to heart and grabbed Bro and lead him off to my apartment.

As fate would have it Bro would act out on a day my moms was off from work. As we walked back to the apartment I was going off on Bro. "Nigga I live here. You can't be coming out here making shit difficult for me. I don't know these niggas like that".

We entered the apartment with Bro in tears. Moms jumped into mother mode "What's wrong, what happened"? Bro asked moms for a bible and she soothed him while they read passages out the good book. She told us that she didn't want anything to happen to him while he was in her care and he needed to go home. Moms gave him some train fare and he caught the bus to the train station.

Trippy

Eric and Holly were stoners. I met them that summer by chance. Somehow they found out I had the killa and were contacting me regularly. We were the same age and went to school together but they had their own apartment in Normandy Village. They were my first white friends. I was surprised to find that they knew me. After we were cool they let me know that I'd met them before at school and after some prodding I was reminded.

Our first encounter was at MC High School in the hall way during a lunch period. They wore oversized clothes that would be tattered. They looked like bums trying to be down with some sort of weird hip hop twist. They wore dread locks and had sandy blonde hair and said, "man and dude" a lot. So, me being me when I saw them at school I started roasting them on site.

I must have went in pretty bad on him because Holly said she stopped me from fighting Eric. I vaguely remember that happening but we were good now.

We smoked lots of reefer in the burning room of their apartment. Yes, they had a room specifically for smoking bud. There were posters on all the walls of trippy things. One poster had a man in a red shirt and blue jeans on a dirt road to nowhere. Sided by green grass the dirt road traveled up the middle to the horizon. Others were black light activated. One looked like a large moon and sun and others were of fish. There was a model airplane on a string in the middle of the ceiling covered in black light paint. Figurines of spiders, frogs, dogs and cats lined the shelves. We sat in bean bag chairs and listened to music like the Doors, Pink Floyd and Jimi Hendrix. There was an assortment of bongs, pipes, rolling papers, and blunts. There were grinders, automatic joint rollers, and one hitters. I'd never seen a smoker's dream room but they'd made that dream a reality.

I was asked over one afternoon and I was presented with the choice to take a hit of acid. My mind raced. I didn't want to become a crackhead. At the same time, I was also fascinated with altered states of reality. Is it actually possible to see things, I wondered? What if I lose my mind? "I don't want to go crazy" I told Eric. I was reassured that as long as I stayed in a happy mind frame it would be cool.

Without much further discussion we all put a half inch piece of paper on our tongues. I was told to just let it dissolve and not to swallow it. As I sat in their living room about to trip off acid I stared out the balcony window overlooking the pool. It was the middle of the afternoon and people were splashing around and laughing in the water.

My attention was brought back when Eric stood and we followed him to the burning room in the back of the apartment. Eric, Holly, and I took a seat in the bean bag chairs closely circled together in the middle of the room. I rolled a joint. Holly stood up and went to get us all a beer. She returned, closed the shades, turned off the lights, passed out the beers, and turned on the black lights.

The room began to glow with colors. The posters lit up with vivid neon colors being extracted by the black light. Greens, pinks, blues, golds and whites beamed. Eric stood up and turned on the airplane. It zipped around in circles above my head. The black light paint that covered the plane caused it to streak in a bright green circular blur.

I fired the joint and we started talking. About a half hour in I was getting upset that nothing had happened. This was bad acid. Someone took his money and sold him paper. I rolled and fired up a blunt. I was seated in front of the poster of the man on the path to nowhere.

The blunt rotated and my gaze stayed on the man to nowhere. By the third rotation the man began to walk up the path. He wasn't in a rush as I figured he knew it would take him a long time to get nowhere at all. The man never advance up the path but the path moved beneath his feet. At a slow and steady pace the grass and dirt road moved as the man walked the path. I looked up to the airplane which was now not just streaking green but doing tricks. The plane looped and flipped and appeared to be flying around the room now. I looked over to Holly then to Eric. I think we all felt it.

Once the acid kicked in we left the burning room and began to tour the house. Our first stop was the bathroom. There was an ocean scene shower curtain with coral reef fish and coral pictured on it. We crowed the small bathroom and stared at the curtain. Without prompting each other, there was a simultaneous inhale and audible "Whoa" as we all experience the fish start moving on the curtain.

It was more like the water in the scene began to sway. Swelling and shrinking in pulses that could be felt in my being as the sea moved. We retreated to the living room. There was a large frog figurine on the table that caught my attention. Its belly began to breathe in and out, slowly. I stood at the mirror by the front door for what could have been hours. I was convinced that I was not just staring back at myself but looking into an alternate reality. As fucked up as I was at that moment. Looking in that mirror really did something to me. I understood at that moment that there was so much more to the world. I knew that what I considered reality was just what I had been shown. I felt there was a large vail over me. I needed to see through it. Staring in that mirror I knew life was so much bigger than me or the little things I do. If I wanted to be successful I would need to be different than anyone I had ever known. I would have to change how things were done for myself and others around me.

We decided to go outside. Why should we keep our underage, drunk and high off of weed and acid, selves in the house? We walked out at the peak of the high. The sun had started to go down as we walked to the middle the parking lot. Step by step laughter bubbled up out of the three of us. We hadn't said a word, but we were laughing like school girls who just saw their first dick. A couple came out of their apartment as we walked by in the street. Someone said "People" and that shit broke us down. For the next hour as we circled the complex we died laughing every time someone would say "People".

We finally made it back to their apartment and we tried to eat but to no success. All the food tasted like clay to me. I wasn't hungry anyway. I was however high as hell. It was going on midnight and I was as high as when it started. We went out on the balcony through the silver colored patio door frame. The balcony was wood, painted brown, and it was just enough room for the three of us.

I found myself peering into space. The night was perfectly clear without a cloud in the sky. Every star looked like a shiny pinpoint in the fabric of existence. Then, the stars started shooting! The star would streak to a point in space, leaving a white trail behind the starting point, and following the star until the white line vanished. When the star found its spot to stop the back end of the trail would catch up with the front of the streak and meet. Hundreds of shooting stars slashed the cosmos that night. I tried to wish on as many as I could. The night grew long and before I knew it 3 am had come up on us. I was still high! I walked home across the plush grass of Normandy to my apartment. I wanted to go to sleep but I was unable to do so as I watched my carpet conveyor belt under my closet door all night. I finally got to sleep and when I awoke I told myself that was some cool shit but never again.

Senior Year

I wanted to drive. I was tired of catching the bus and waiting in the freezing cold or the summer heat. I didn't have a driver's license but that didn't matter much to me. I was about to start school in a week and I needed a car. I looked through the classified ads and found an 83 Ford Crown Victoria LTD for $400. I got KD to take me to address listed and I talked to the seller and we settled on $350. It was a brick red color and rag top was peeling, splitting, and cracking. Rust had eaten through the bottom of all the 4 doors. It was missing 2 of the hub caps. When the car started it revved, squeaked, and shook. The car was a piece of shit, but I didn't care. It drove and that's all that mattered. I had KD follow me back to the apartment because I didn't have a license plate. I backed the car in and parked the car in front of my apartment.

I waited for night fall. I needed a license plate and I set my mind to steal one. The parking lot of the complex was too open for me to take a plate off of someone's car so I walked to the houses that neighbored the complex. There was a house that I had walked pass a million times on my way to the gas station that had 4 cars in the driveway. All I had to do was take the plate off one of them and that is what I did. The cars in the long driveway reached all the way to the street. Dressed in all black, I sat on the ground behind a white minivan. I took the license plate. I put it in my large hoodie front pocket and walked back to the complex. Without a second thought I put it on my new car.

I sacked up a dub of bud and called my guy to help me christen the ride. I stopped at the gas station to get a few swishers. I pulled off and hit the main road in town, Franklin St. I had stolen a few cars before but didn't really know the rules of the road.

The car's muffler had a hole in it so it was extremely loud. It needed a wheel alignment bad because it pulled hard to the right when I hit the gas. I was in traffic swerving in and out of the lanes trying to keep the car straight.

We made it about 10 blocks on Franklin St. before out of nowhere saw red and blue lights behind me. I immediately passed the sack of killa to my man. He then stuffed it under the seat as I pulled over. I was asked by the officer for my license and registration. I had neither.

At gun point we were ordered out of the car. I was told that the license plate didn't match the car as the other officer checked the inside of the car. I told the officer "I just bought the car this morning and the plate came with the car. The owner told me I could keep the plate until I got my own". The officer fumbling through the inside came back with the sack of killa that was under the seat. He shined the flashlight on it and asked "what's this". As dumbfounded as I could look I replied "What is that"? "It looks like marijuana to me", he said. "Marijuana? I don't smoke marijuana.

I just bought the car today. That was already in here," I told him. The officer told me he was going to have to tow the car but he would let us go. The officer even gave my friend and I a ride back to Normandy Village. I was given a ticket for driving with no license and a date to show up in court. My court date was the first day of school of my senior year. That's going to play well in my plan to be fresh on the first day of school.

The first day of school rolled around like a Dayton wires. I was ready and had my red Polo shirt and red Pelle' Pelle' jeans shorts pressed and creased. I had spoken to my man and he agreed to go to court with me for support. We hopped on the bus early in the morning on our way to court. I hadn't let my mother know because I'd only gotten a ticket and it wasn't a big deal.

We entered the courthouse which was just a few steps from the bus stop. I stood in a respectable manner in line as I waited for the secretary to call me so I may handle my business. I walked up when called and told her I had gotten this ticket, which I presented to her. She asked my name and I told her.

I looked at my man, who was hugging the wall and watching me handle my business and gave him a nod of reassurance. I was then tapped on my shoulder by a large white man in a button up shirt and a badge on his belt. He asked if my name was Dasism Lord and I said yes. I then noticed his large black friend whom was dressed just like him with a button up shirt and dark slacks with a badge on his belt. They let me know that I needed to get out of line.

My man slowly faded to the background. I didn't even try to make eye contact with him as I was handcuffed. I was read my rights in the hallway of the court house. I was told I was being arrested for being in possession of stolen property. In the back of my head I thought, "Damn, the fucking license plate!" What came out my mouth was "what stolen property"?

I was paraded through the halls of the courthouse in front of everyone waiting to go to court. I was guided out the front door and passed my man who was standing on the steps. We walked down the sidewalk of a main street as cars passed and the people ogled.

We crossed the street after we waited for the light to turn green. All the while I was handcuffed behind my back and being led by two burly officers whom felt good showing off the bad guy to the community. Once across the street I was aimed into the police station. I was finger printed and once they found out how old I was after a long debate. My mother was called. Damn, damn again!

My mother had no clue of what I was doing today. As far as she knew I was at school. Now she had to come to the station to get me out of jail. Moms doesn't have a car so she had to catch the bus to come get me and that takes at least an hour. As I sat in the jail cell for the second time of my life, I began to ponder what she would do once she got to me. I thought about me being a lifelong offender that had a destiny to be a fuck up, never getting away, but always getting caught. Then I heard my name. I came out and was released to moms.

Moms didn't say a word to me as we walked out the police station. We crossed the street and walked pass the courthouse I'd been taken from, to the bus stop in front of the library. We sat in the fiber glass covered bus stop shelter and waited for what seemed like an eternity. The bus arrived with a grumble and screech and I entered the bus first. She paid my fare and sat a few rows in front of me.

This whole time she hadn't spoken one word to me nor looked in my direction. I studied my mom's facial expression and her body posture. She was beyond pissed and I knew I would be in for her full wrath. The furl in her brow and the pucker of her lips said more than she could ever express with words.

Normandy Village appeared on the horizon and my heartbeat began to increase as we pulled into the complex. We exited the bus and walked over the perfectly manicured lawn that felt like plush carpet under my feet. As I walked down the stone steps to my apartment I could hear every rock and pebble scratch the steps. Over the green all weather carpet and wood grained lined hallway that led to my door seem to stretch on and on forever. She had been in front of me the whole walk and her small but powerful legs pushed her body forward with a sense of urgency. The keys came out of her oversized purse and she entered the apartment.

We secured our front door with a door club. This was a tool used to stop an intruder from entering your home through the front door. It was a metal pipe with a U-shaped end that would go under the door knob and the other end was like a door stop. We'd jam it under the door knob at night and feel safe. Once I came through the door it closed behind me and mom's grabbed the door club. With a quick swing, she hit me in the back with the club. Her aim got good and hit my ribs and legs. I dodged and countered. She screamed while her eyes bulged out of her face. Her hair was wild and stringy as she went in on how I was a disappointment. With every verbal jab came a swing of the door club. One to the head and I was done. I grabbed the door club and we fought over it until I overpowered moms. I bellowed out "STOP! I know I messed up but you can't hit me like this!" I don't remember what happened after that. I did know if I was going to hustle and be about that life, I would need to get on my square.

My senior year didn't start off how I had imagined. I thought I would be pulling up in my first car and getting all the bitches... well that didn't happen. I did however make it a point to be known in MC High School. KD and I were close. He had a girlfriend and she was a pretty red bone. They were on and off for a while because she was loose and fucking other dudes. She started fucking with the nigga Shannon. Shannon was a bitch made nigga. I mean to the core he was a hoe. He'd be doing comedy and shit at school for the talent shows. I really didn't know Shannon other than KD didn't like him. That was good enough for me; I didn't like him either off the strength of KD.

KD had been talking about getting in Shannon's ass for taking his girl. I was king instigator so I gassed him up every time he brought it up to me. I was about that life. I thrived off of drama, intimidation, and what I loved best... the demonstration!

We went to the bowling alley one weekend because that's what we did in MC. The first person we saw was Shannon at the arcade playing a seated driving game. I nudged KD and nodded my head as to point out Shannon. Shannon had a few of his guys with him watching him play. KD and I walked behind him. I mugged his boys and they looked up then back down quickly. KD knew I had his back and I saw for the first time "that look" in his eye. KD reached around to the front of Shannon and smacked the brim of his fitted ball cap. Shannon looked back at KD with a frown and then noticed me. He turned back around and attempted to play the game. KD smacked the brim again. Shannon jumped up and confronted KD. In one fluid motion KD scooped Shannon between his legs and flexed him onto the bowling ball rack. Balls everywhere!

The police ran up and I start explaining that Shannon hit KD. That didn't happen at all, but the second cop cosigned me. "Yeah, that guy hit this guy and then he body slammed him" is what he told the other cop. So much happen to me in that moment in time because for the first time in my life I realized memories could be implanted. Everything happened so fast that the cop didn't know what happened. I spoke up first and seeded his memory with false information that he believed to have happen. Wow! Not only that but I saw KD get down and hold his own. Shannon went to jail because he was over 18 and KD got released to his moms.

Up until now I hadn't had to demonstrate on anyone in MC. I was getting my money off of killa. I was trying to fuck with the bitches. Hell, I'd gotten more pussy in MC than anywhere else I'd lived.

I never worried about or was intimidated by anybody in MC. They were slow compared to the life I'd already lived. I knew they had never or may never experience what I'd been through. I was seasoned and hard. I'd been shot at and I've shot at. I thought I had an understanding of moving in the streets. KD's fight with Shannon was the start of a bigger beef.

At lunch hour, I hung out with a small group of friends that welcomed me into their group. They'll never know how much I appreciated them for letting me kick it and not making me feel awkward. We were a small band, but it was love. One of the couples got married and the husband is a police officer now. I won't name them, but they know who they are... THANKS!

I saw Shannon come through the ROTC doors that connected to the lunch room. I burst into a heavy bellow of laughter. He walked right passed me and I laughed even louder. I began telling stories of how KD beat that ass at the bowling alley last weekend. Shannon got mad and stopped. I asked him "What the fuck you stop for? You saw what KD did to you. What do you think Im'a do?" Shannon blew up and got to talking shit. I took off my earring and necklace and passed it to my girl.

Shannon started walking off back through the ROTC doors. I followed through the doors and began talking louder. He stopped walking and we confronted each other. By the time we got face to face the ROTC teacher came out and stopped us. With the class behind him watching the action, he said "Dasism what are you doing? You want to get suspended again? Don't do this. I know you can beat him and you know you can beat him. You don't have anything to prove."

With that validation being broadcast to the class behind him, I was good. He grabbed Shannon and told him to leave. "Don't you have a job to go to? You need to go." Shannon walked out the back door of the school. I thought he was going to work. He went to school half the day and worked the other half. I felt good. I felt hard. I poked my chest out a little more because even the teachers knew I was about that life. What a day!

I took the bus home that day as usual. I remember it was cooler out that day because I had my oversized coat. The bus pulled up to Normandy Village and I departed the bus talking to a girl I was trying to holla at. As soon as I walked off the bus I noticed 2 box Chevy Caprices in front of the head office. They looked out of place and as I walked down the driveway 8 people climbed out of the cars. I didn't know any of these grown men except for the 3 who went to my school. I stopped in my tracks and threw off my coat.

In as confrontational of a stance as I could posture I bellowed, "What the fuck, you need all these niggas to come for me? Let's go!" I knew I would have been beaten badly but I didn't care. I knew I would fuck a couple of them up before it was over for me. Then in a bitch ass move, one of the grown men pulled up his shirt and showed the pistol tucked in his pants. What was going on... all these niggas and he going to pull a chopper? Wow! I started running through the football field sized lawn. I cut through the apartment hallways. In one hallway and out another I ran. Back onto the grass I ran up on Shannon finding him alone. I rushed him. All the other guys began pouring through the halls running up on me again. I fled to my apartment. Realizing halfway there I didn't have my keys because I'd dropped my coat at the entrance by the bus stop. I kept running to my nigga Tate's apartment.

Tate was a nigga from the G. He was a light skinned pretty boy. He had a black Trans Am, fucked with the bitches, and smoked weed. Tate was an old school nigga who didn't play games and thought shit through. Tate lived on the third floor, so I hustled up the steps and banged on his door for my life. He opened the door and pulled me in knowing something was wrong. I explained what was going on and why I couldn't get in my house because I left my keys. I asked him for a chopper. Tate took me to his balcony window and pulled back the blinds. He asked me "Das, what do you see?" I looked out the window and looked down to see one of the Chevys' driving through the sea of green grass. The tires were ripping it out as the tires spun which made the engine roar. Midway through a doughnut, grass flying everywhere, they got stuck. Tate said "see Das, they ain't ready. You don't need a chopper for them. Look at em! We could pick them all off right now. Don't worry about that." All of his guys had come to the distressed cars' rescue. 6 niggas behind the car pushing it out of the mud hole it created as we watched from above. They were none the less aware of where I was but I felt empowered. They were stupid. I was not. They needed all those people for me. I was a one-man army. Fuck what they are on. I'll get them back!

Little did they know but it was not over, and I would get my vindication. I began to broadcast to whoever would listen that I was coming for Shannon and his boys. I wanted it to get back to him or his boys, so they knew when they saw me it was a problem. I spent the weekend doing pushups and swinging my dumbbells for speedy fists and knockout power. I couldn't wait to get to school on Monday morning. I wore my brand new red Nike hooded sweatshirt and black jeans. I couldn't think of anything else other than catching one of them, all of them. I was either going to get beat up or I was going to beat somebody's ass bad. Whatever the case I was ready for it.

I made a B line straight to my locker and got my books. I then began to prowl the halls for the first one I saw be it Shannon or one of his friends. I walked around the first corner in front of the main office and I saw Al. Al was one of Shannon's boys. He was stalky and built and looked like a football player. He stood about 6 feet with a short-tapered fade haircut. We locked eyes. I dropped my books to the floor. My heart raced and my palms began to sweat. I balled my right hand into a fist and with my left hand I grabbed his collar. With everything I had in me I hit him in the jaw still holding his collar. Again, and again I unleased a flurry of rights to his face. He began swinging wildly and caught me with a strong left to the eye. We fell into the girls' bathroom. The crowd began to gather and with a glance of the crowd I could see the principal and other teachers watching the fight. They never tried to intervene. That was cool with me as I got back into the moment. I let him go and began to stomp him out. Al balled up in the fetal position on the floor and stopped fighting back. I won! As cool as I could be I grabbed my books and began to walk to class. A few steps in, I was grabbed up by the principal and taken to the office.

I had been in the office many times before and he felt like he knew me. He felt like he could influence me. He thought he knew better for me and my situation because he'd seen kids like me before. Little did he know he'd never met anyone like ME. He began to ask me how I felt about school. "Is school too hard for you? You are at the age where you don't have to be here if you don't want to. You can withdraw yourself. What do you think about that?" I stared at him for a while and thought to myself…can he ask me this? I answered, "School is not hard."

Then Shannon and a few of his boys came charging in the office. They were rowdy like they were about to do something. The principal calmed him down and sent his boys out the office. He sat Shannon and I down and asked us to squash the beef. I never said a word. Then he proceeded to tell us both that we'd be expelled for the rest of the school year if we didn't agree right now. We both agreed. Al never came back to school after getting whooped in front of all his peers. I didn't know them niggas in MC like that but they sure knew me after I put down that Al demonstration.

Shannon and the rest of his boys stayed away from me the rest of the time I was at MC high. I remember in the summer after the fight I saw Shannon in Normandy Village. KD and I were together walking around the complex smoking a blunt and there he was. I started taunting him. "What the fuck you doing out here? You don't belong out here. You should go now!"

Shannon tried to hold his own but to no avail. As soon as he started talking I picked up a rock and threw it at his head. KD picked up a rock and pitched it at his body. Laughing and throwing rocks we pelted Shannon. He tried to protect himself and balled up in the corner of the building. I never saw Shannon again.

The Come Up

When my brother passed away I was a beneficiary on his life insurance policy. Since I was underage at the time it was put into an account that I'd be able to access at the age of 18. I turned 18 by the end of my senior year in April. I got a check in the mail for $13K. I was 18 and now I had racks to spend. The very first thing I did was go to the car lot and bought a 1989 Chevy Blazer. It was all black with leather seats, a moon roof, and four-wheel drive. I didn't have a driver's license but the dealer didn't care because I had cash money. I was now ready. I bought my mother the rocking chair she'd asked for since I was a boy. I got a Rolex necklace with matching bracelet and a big dumb ass gold nugget earring. I was shitting on everyone. I was full baller now and you could see it.

All I needed were some deep bass throbbing speakers. I called Big Cuzzo. He was living in Indianapolis and was a wiz in electronics and computers. I hated sitting around the hood. I never liked living in Indy but I did like the thick ass women in Indianapolis. My nigga June was down for the trip. We got a sack of bud and hit 65 South. We smoked the entire 2 hours down to Indy. I'd lived out there, so I knew my way around the highways and city streets. Big Cuzzo was there ready for me and we took a trip one of the big box electronic stores. We made B Line to the speakers in the back of the store.

Nothing but the best for me. I had a debit card full of money and I was going to spend it. I was determined to spend it. Cerwin Vegas were as good as it got in the line of speakers. I bought 2 twelve inch subwoofers. I bought a brand-new speaker box with the see-through fiber glass window. You could see orange rimmed speakers throbbing, with a view!

Got the wires, the largest gauge wires they had, and a 1,000-watt amp. We got the tweeters for the highs and new 6x10's for the mid-range. I got a large screen removable flip screen radio with the remote control and CD changer. I went down the CD aisle and got new music. I was like a kid in a candy store. I'd always wanted to have "that car". You know the car all the little kids point at, the one all the girls want to roll in. I was on my way. Wait till I put this beat in the truck!

We piled the cart with supplies and the workers brought the rest to the front. At the checkout lane, there was a OG looking nigga standing there taking in the spectacle of speakers and equipment. He told me he'd sell me everything in his car right now for half of what I was about to pay at the checkout. I wasn't feeling it so I brushed him off and waited my turn in line. The OG left the store.

He pulled his purple candy painted Monte Carlo sitting on something chrome in front of the store and turned his speakers up to full volume. I could feel the bass under my feet. It was vibrating the front of the store. I waved him off again, but I thought maybe I should buy the OG's speakers. It was my turn in line and I paid $2300 for new speaker equipment.

We went back to Big Cuzzo's apartment got the tools ready and began to dismantle the inside of the Black Blazer. We unscrewed the baseboards, pulled of the inside panels to the dashboard. The hood was open and wires got hooked to my battery and strung through the inside of the truck under the exposed baseboards. Power from the battery was wired and screwed to the amps. The amps were wired to speakers. Small 2-inch tweeters were put into the side panels up by my ears when seated in the truck.

Smaller factory speakers were taken out the doors and larger 6x10's was installed. The old radio was removed and the brand-new high-tech LED radio made the inside of the car glow. We put the Cerwin Vega's into the speaker box and screwed it down, then connected the clear fiber glass covering. The wires from the amp went to the subwoofers to give them power. It was time.

I put in the triple CD Lost by 8Ball, Mystikal Unpredictable, and Master P's The Ice Cream Man into the CD changer. The Ice Cream Man was the first song ever played in the now beating Black Blazer. The sun was coming up as we'd worked through the night. Big Cuzzo tweaked the levels, checked wires, and gave me an overview of what I could but shouldn't do. I thanked him and I hit the highway gasping for breath as my beat bumped.

I wanted to get back as soon as I could so I could show off. The beat hit so hard all my mirrors shook to the point that they were of no help because I could not see out of them do to the vibration. Surges of deep bass penetrated my chest and ear-piercing symbols coming from the highs by my ears. It sounded like I was inside a concert, inside my own truck.

By the time we made it back to the Circle, we had gone through all the songs in the changer. I pulled down the block slow. Car alarms were being set off as I passed with an earth quaking beat coming out my truck. Crisp and deep I rumbled the street. I pulled up and I saw smiling faces but they didn't look happy in their eyes.

Eyes tell it all and I can see you. I was proud but the look on the faces of my friends... was envy. I was confused. I'd be happy for my friend. I didn't think much on it as I showed off everything I'd just bought. They crowded around and took good inspection of the new sounds. Criticism came from all the old heads about what I could have done or should have bought. They were mad and faking it with me. I saw it.

Burnt

I'd make frequent trips back and forth to the G in my shiny Blazer. I bought a .9 mm Carbine rifle. In Indiana, you can legally buy a rifle and carry it at 18. The bull shit was you had to be 21 years old to buy bullets. What the fuck was that about? It didn't matter I still got some bullets.

I'd keep the Carbine with me as I'd broken the hammer on the .22 by accident and it was worthless but I kept it around just in case I found a sucker to sell it to. On a trip to the G, I'd decided to go early in the morning and bend a few blocks. I was riding down 21st Ave. by the alternative school on the west side when I saw I sassy little brown skin girl switching her ass like her pussy was wet because she was just gliding. I turned the beat up to get noticed and she looked up and followed my truck with her whole head turning as I rode pass her.

I bent a block and came back to where she was walking. I pulled up and rolled down the window. I spit a little game and she got in the truck. We talked and she told me she was going to her house in DHB. I thought damn she is far from home but I took her to her house. We went into the house and I sat as she took a shower and changed clothes. She gave me a peek at her ass as she was changing and my dick grew instantly. Nothing sexual happened, we got back in the truck and bent some blocks.

I took her to the hood as I wanted to show the fellas the fine piece of ass I'd just acquired. We went to Playboys house. Playboy was a dark-skinned Michael Jordan look alike. Playboy was put in a situation that no one should have to deal with.

I don't know the details but his mother left him abandoned in their house. We were all hustling so we kept him fed and high. Since he had the house to himself we took it upon ourselves to turn it into the spot. This is where we kick it, sell our dope, and fuck bitches.

I pulled up with Lil Chocolate and went into the house. June, Loco, and Playboy were there when we came into the basement. We entered the first room on the left. I pulled out a condom she pulled down her pants. I laid on the ground and she mounted me. A few minutes into fucking, all my niggas all piled into the room.

They huddled around us. She didn't miss a stroke as she kept fucking to the audience we had just gained and I was with it too. They all started grabbing and trying to fondle her which I didn't care too much about until someone touched me. "Whoa! Yall niggas gone to have to chill out. You are touching me and shit!" I screamed out to them. They all stopped, and someone fired up a blunt.

We fucked and smoked while talking shit to the niggas in the room. She was riding me for what seemed like an hour when I started getting upset because I hadn't cum yet. In an act of desperation and peer pressure to finish I pulled the condom off and bust a nut in a few strokes. Night had fallen and I was ready to go home. They all tried to fuck too but she wasn't with it as I'd been fucking her for a good hour and I know she was sore. She asked that I take her home and I obliged. After dropping her off I went back home in MC.

I'd never played with a girl like Lil Chocolate before and I wanted to fuck her some more. I'd fantasize about the brown of her skin and the chocolate of her erect nipples. Her perfect bubble booty was soft and jiggled when I smacked it. I wanted to see that ass again. Maybe I'd get a room the next time so I wouldn't have to deal with my niggas.

I was also messing with a female I had befriended before I moved from the G. I was only at Roosevelt for 3 months before I moved but I did meet a few new girls. This one in particular was the daughter of a funeral home director. She was a high yellow big girl with massive breasts. She liked my brother before he passed and for some reason she liked me too.

From the time I moved out of the G she was always in the background fighting for time. I liked Yellow. She was mature. She was going to be my first back in the day but it didn't work out like it should have. We were in an abandoned house on lunch hour trying to fuck. Someone outside screamed "police coming" and everyone in an abandoned house ran out.

I was to meet with Yellow and she came to pick me up from the apartment in MC. We went back to the G and I smoked as she drove. She wanted to fuck so she pulled up next to the highway in a secluded location. By chance I brushed my dick with my hand as I maneuvered in the small white Neon. I'd never felt that before so I excused myself, explaining that I needed to piss.

I stood outside the car and attempted to examine my dick on the side of the road. It was stuck to the inside of my underwear. There was some kind of secretion coming out also. I got back in the car and told her I need to go home now. She was confused and disappointed that we were not going to fuck but I insisted to go home, NOW.

When I got in the house I made a B-line to the bathroom. I peeled my dick from my underwear again and attempted to piss. "OH! AH! SHIT!" I yelled out as I tried to pee. The sensation of hundreds of tiny needles poking the inside of my pee hole almost brought me to tears. I wrapped my dick in toilet paper so it would not stick to my underwear anymore. I went to bed. When I awoke in the morning a thick white puss was coming out of my dick. It soaked the toilet paper and coated the inside of my underwear. I went into the bathroom as I had done for many years in the past to take my early morning piss. This morning was different. Burning needles filled my dick with pain as my urine trickled out at a snail's pace. I moaned and groaned as quietly as I could as I didn't want moms asking me what was wrong. I rolled a blunt and smoked thinking about what I needed to do. I had to go to the clinic.

I went to the local clinic, filled out the paper work and took a seat in the lobby. I felt nasty and dirty. I was contaminated. What was this I have? Why is my dick dripping goo? When I find that bitch I'm going to kill her. Is this curable? Why are they taking so long? Fuck this I'm good. After waiting for over an hour I got up and left the clinic. My dick was still sick but somehow, I figured I could fix it. I went home and tried to piss. "FUCK! OH! SHIT!" I screamed in pain. How could I think I can fix this? What was I going to do? I woke up in the morning bright and early and went back to the clinic. I didn't care how long they took I was going to sit there until I was called.

"Dasism" I heard my name ring out by the nurse. I walked back to be examined. I explained what the problem was and the nurse needed to see it. So much shame entered my spirit as I pulled my sick dick out to show a female nurse. She looked at it and told me the doctor would have to take a culture to be sure of what it was.

The nurse walked out and several minutes later the doctor walked into the room. He pulled out a large Q tip looking stick with cotton on each side of it. He explained that he would need to put the cotton end into the tip of my dick. Wait, what did he just say? Put the cotton in my pee hole? What?

The doctor cleaned off the crusted puss that had dried on my dick. He took the Q tip and pushed about an inch of it in my pee hole. OH MY GOD! That is a feeling I cannot describe but I can tell you no man wants to feel something going into a hole that stuff should be coming out of. I was told that he thinks I have the clap. I was given a shot in the ass and a prescription for penicillin. I got my pills and my problem went away. I would never have sex without protection again. Sick dick ain't cool!

It had been about a week since I had gotten burnt and now I was ok. I got a call from the hood. I was told that Lil Chocolate had been back to the hood and Playboy was cuffing her in the house. She'd been over there for a few days without a change of clothes and there was no running water at his house so I could imagine the funk coming out of her pussy.

I wanted to tell them to run! I'd just been burnt by her. Don't fuck! I was then reassured that no one could get at her as Playboy had locked the doors to the spot. He wasn't letting them in and he'd been going in on a 2 day fuck a thon. Playboy didn't have a phone so I couldn't warn him without letting the niggas know. I wasn't going to put him on blast like that so I kept it in until I saw him. I didn't get back to the hood until about a week later.

I pulled up on his house. Before I could open my door, Playboy opened his front door and started jogging down the steps toward the Blazer. He opened the door "Your shit leaking ain't it" he asked? I shook my head and smirked. He got in.

I explained to him that my shit was leaking but not anymore. I told him he has the clap and needs to go to the doctor to get some pills and a shot in the ass. I then told him that if he hadn't been running behind the bitches I fucked, only I would have to worry about being burnt. But no, you had to fuck too.

I was highly upset that I'd been burnt by a dirty bitch. I was going to find her and one day we did. Bro, Playboy and I were bending blocks one afternoon when Playboy spotted her walking down Virginia St. I turned around and dropped off Bro. He didn't need to be involved in this.

I didn't know what I was going to do but I was going to do something. I sped back to find her before her car hopping ass got picked up by some other unsuspecting swinging dick bound to be burnt too. I pulled up and tried to get her to get in the truck. She resisted. I told her I had some weed and we can smoke. She hopped right in the front as Playboy got in the back.

We rolled up to Carolina Park. The court was full of the fellas running a whole court game. I parked under my usual spot under the shade tree. The windows were down and the breeze blew in, I stalled. My mind raced about what I was going to do. I gave Playboy the look.

I thought about my dick being sick and how she could have given me something more serious. My blood boiled, my muscles tighten, I open my door, stepped out and took a breath.

I looked at Lil Chocolate and she looked at me. With a swift Jonny Cage kick to the side of her body she flew out of the door of the Blazer. Her Jordan came off in the process of her flying through the door. I ran around to the other side of the truck as Playboy jumped out the backseat. I grabbed her shirt and pulled it off of her. In her bare bra and dirty white pants with one shoe on, Playboy grabbed the Jordan left in the front seat on the passenger side and began to beat her in the head with it.

I reached back in the truck to the very back where I kept my Carbine. I pulled it out and fished around for the clip in the glove box. I started seeing everything as it was in slow motion. Everyone had stopped playing basketball as they watched the demonstration unfolding before their eyes. I saw the mail lady trying not to pay attention but she was watching. I saw the little kids by the swings looking at the half naked woman getting beat with the shoe.

I snapped back to reality and fumbled to put the clip in the gun. I walked out into full view as I attempted to load the gun. "Don't do that D! She had enough! Don't shoot her!" could be heard from the court. I looked around again and thought you can't do this in front of everyone. I got back in my truck and drove back to the hood.

A crazy ending to the saga of Lil Chocolate was that somewhere around 10 months after the incident Playboy and I went to the Village Shopping Center on a humbug. As we walked in there was a female sitting on the bench with a new born baby in her arms. I looked at Playboy and asked "Ain't that old girl?" He shook his head and we started laughing. I started teasing him that that was his baby. He teased me that it was mine. To this day I don't know if that was her sitting on the bench waiting. Playboy or I may have been the daddy to the baby, I'll never know.

Legend of the Black Truck

I was comfortable with my travel back and forth from MC to the G. I made the trips whenever I wanted to chill out when my boys or if I needed re up on weed. I was still trying to show and prove on the block so if I got a call that my nigga was in need I'd be there to aid and assist. That call came in one night from Loco.

He'd been beefing with some guy in Miller and wanted to ride on him. I pulled up and Loco, Playboy, June, and some nigga that was Loco's guy got in and we plotted. The mission was to roll up on the targets house in Miller pull him out and whoop his ass. I didn't know who we were about to roll on but it didn't matter.

We got some Paul Masson and started drinking as we rolled through the night streets. It takes about 20 minutes to get from the East Side to Miller so by the time we navigated to the house we were all ready for whatever. I had my Carbine and Loco had a .9 mm High Point pistol. I pulled up on the opposite side of the street directly across from the house. Loco and Playboy got out and ran across the street. We were all in black as it was our uniform. We wore black daily never knowing what might jump off any given day.

I watched as Loco unscrewed the motion detector light that came on as they walked up the side of the house. I saw Loco knock on the door like the police. Bang! Bang! Bang! He pounded on the door. It was silent outside.

He walked around to the oversized glass windows and started beating on them. Clank! Clank! Clank! He rattled the windows. I thought he might break them. Then silence again. This time the silence was broken by a deafening alarm that could have awoken the dead. They ran back to the truck and jumped in as I pulled off without lights. As we got around the corner I turned my lights on and asked "What the fuck was that? Was that an alarm?"

We drove a few blocks and realized that we were hot, as a police car passed us going the other way. I let the police car go a few blocks and I pulled over and told Loco to get out the truck. He took the liquor, weed, and the guns. We shook hands and I pulled off.

I stopped at the next stop sign and made a left on Lake St. right in front of the entrance to the apartments. I drove a block and pulled over again. I wanted to post up and watch for police. I could see Loco in my rear-view mirror far back in the cut. I hit my break lights to give him the signal to come on so we could leave. As soon as I hit my break lights... police pulled up out of nowhere.

The police car lit the block with it strobe lights of red and blue. This was no party though. The first thing out the policeman's mouth was "Who is Loco?" We all looked around at each other, puzzled. Loco? I repeated to the officer. "I don't know a Loco." He went on to tell me how he wasn't stupid and he knew one of us was Loco. We were all pulled out of the truck, ordered to our knees and handcuffed as they searched the Blazer. I sat quietly as they searched I knew they wouldn't find anything. June sat quietly too.

The officer asked Playboy where Loco was. Playboy started laughing which didn't amuse the officer one bit. The officer checked his skull hat and put it back on his head and Playboy started laughing harder. The officer hit Playboy in the stomach. The other nigga with us was Loco's boy. He must have had a warrant or something because he was placed in the back of the police car. I didn't care. He wasn't my dude. What was funny was, as the police told me I needed to "take my ass back to MC," I could still see Loco in the cut watching the whole demonstration. I pulled off behind the police and followed them for a while as the police station is on the way to the hood. They took a turn they shouldn't have. I never knew what happened to Loco's boy. I never saw him again.

I never lost my ties to the streets. As a matter of fact, while in MC I was catching the train every week to the G to re up. I got right into the groove. The first person I recall pulling up on me was Mikeo. Mikeo stood about 5 foot 8 inches of thug nigga. He had corn rolls to the back and kept an "I don't give a fuck" expression on his face. Mikeo was my brother's friend and a few years older than me. He picked me up the day my brother was killed and took me to the Color Doors. He was also one of the shooters in front of the school when Loco and I saw the car get shot up.

I heard his car blocks before it appeared in front of the house. He was driving a sunset colored Monte Carlo. The paint was a solid burnt orange at the top and faded to a white at the bottom of the car. He was rolling on cheese balls, Gold Dayton's, and vogue tires. Mikeo asked me to roll with him.

I hooped in and my breath was immediately taken away as the bass throbbed through my body. The bass was so loud and deep it truly messed with my breathing but I manned up and started nodding my head to the beat. As we rolled around the G, I felt important and cool. I knew everyone we rode pass wanted to be in the car.

They wanted to be us. All the females we went by looked in the car to see who was banging so hard. This is what I'd been waiting for, the life of a baller, thug, and hustler. We pulled up on 20 Block.

Mikeo pulled out a Back Wood cigar and rolled up a blunt. We sat back and smoked while he put me onto game. He told me that he didn't want people to know we were good like that and he had my back. He let me know they was getting money and I could come to the block and get money too.

We started talking about my brother, Ralph. He let me know that the dudes he was kicking it with back in the day were lame and after my brother got killed they all left and it was just him and his brother. He told me to watch niggas because they not getting money and they are jealous. One thing I learned about Mikeo early was that he spoke his mind and didn't care if you like what he said or not because he was being honest. I respected that in him. He kept it real all-day long.

I was never stuck in a box. I was always able to get money in the circle with my 16th crew, I could go to the End and freelance by bending blocks and looking for the geekers, or I could go to 20 Block to sell. I was respected but mostly on the strength of my brother. I was getting money on a regular.

If I wasn't going to the G, I spent my time in Normandy Village driving around the complex bumping my music. On more than one occasion they would come from the office to wherever I was to ask me to turn my music down because they'd been getting complaints. I'd turn it down for a little while.

I'd pull off and go to a different part of the complex, start politicking with someone else, and turn up the volume. Once again, they'd find me and ask to turn down the music. I got quick with the turn off button in traffic too. Police didn't like that banging music and would pull you over if they heard it.

MC had the beachfront. On Sunday evenings, the beach was the place to be. It was like a car show. The women were out in little a bit of nothing and the niggas were stunting for attention. My truck stood out big time.

My 13 inch spokes poked out the side about 6 inches. It looked like the Black Blazer squatted on the rims and pushed them out the side. The bass was just right to catch all the attention. Damn, it felt good to be a gangsta...

Getting attention was part of the dope boy code and it was my turn. I awoke one morning and got myself together as usual. I grabbed my sack of bud and my radio face. It was a perfect summer morning. I unlocked the door and adjusted the seat. It was unusual because no one drove the truck other than me.

I connected the face of the radio to the radio and clicked it into place. I put the key in the ignition and cranked up the Black Blazer. It cranked up the first time. I adjusted my rearview mirror. I thought to myself, wow, my back window is awfully clean as I peered into the rear view reflection. I looked down at the radio and turned up the volume. I turned it up some more but all I could hear was the speakers under the dashboard.

I looked into the rearview mirror again but this time I noticed the hydraulic pump that allowed the back window to open and close without slamming, was hanging. I turned around in my seat and immediately felt the breeze from the outside blow against my face. I hadn't opened any windows.

The back window was shattered into thousands of tiny glass squares and rectangles. All in the back of the truck. The rubber frame that was around the window, used to insulate the inside of the truck from the rain, hung and swayed in the wind. Tiny glass shards remained affixed to the rubber frame that once held a whole window.

I got out the truck and went to the back of it. The back of the truck had scratch marks and gouges from having the lock removed by crow bar. Where there was once a lock was now an empty hole. I opened the lift gate. My speakers were gone. My speaker box was gone. My amp was gone. Wires were pulled and my baseboards were pulled out the frames. I had also left my .9mm Carbine in the truck. It was also gone.

This was the first time I had been robbed, but it wasn't the last. My gun and my speakers were gone. I was upset for a while then I realized being mad about it wasn't going to get it back for me. Why did I have all that equipment without an alarm system? All I could do was hustle. That's what I did I met more people and sold more weed. I was back in position and able to replace the speaker system.

Phoenix

Up and down the highway I traveled anytime I thought about it. It was a sunny summer day so I asked Bro and June to roll to Indianapolis with me. June had to work that day but I didn't know that until later. We got some bud and rolled up a 5 pack of Swisher Blunts.

I hit 65 South speeding down the highway. The Black Blazer only had 85 MPH on the speedometer. There was an orange needle behind the window showing the speedometer that would disappear if went faster than 85. I had that little orange needle buried the entire trip until we hit some rain.

In Indiana, there are a lot of open fields unless you are in one of the urban cities. Riding down state is a trip through farmland and nothing more. Thunderstorms and tornados can pop up quickly. We were caught in a torrential rainfall. Cars were pulling over to the side of the road and people were hiding under the underpasses outside of their cars. I wondered why everyone was taking such caution. It didn't matter, I had a 4X4 and it was cutting through the rain.

The brightest light I've ever seen came out of the sky and hit my truck. I was blinded. The radio stopped playing and the truck shook. We were hit by a lightning bolt. My heart pumped out of my chest. I tried to focus as I pulled off the highway to the side of the road like all the other cars. Another blunt was fired up and again smoke filled the air. I jumped over the back seat to check my speakers. The fuse had blown in the amp. I changed the fuse, the rain subsided, and we continued to Indy.

When we got to Indy the sun was shining and the weather was beautiful. I got off the highway on 38th St. At the first stop light, we pulled up next to a car full of beautiful women. I turned the bass up to get their attention. Bro rolled the window down and spoke to the women.

They wanted to smoke and kick it too. They told us to follow them to the park. We trailed them to a park that was full of people. We got out, fired up a blunt and began chopping it up with the women. It was one for us all and they were all beautiful and thick. The blunt made its final rotation and phone numbers were exchanged. My day was going great and I had just met some women.

I didn't want to drive back in the dark so we went back to the gas station and filled the tank, took a piss, and got some Swisher Sweet Blunts. I turned the air conditioner up to full blast, turned the music up to full volume, got on the highway, and buried the needle to full speed. 30 minutes into the trip both June and Bro were sleeping. I flipped through songs and CD's while dipping in and out of traffic.

An hour into the trip as I changed lanes to pass a slower car I heard a loud POP. What was that I yelled out loud. My steering wheel got stiff and I was slowing down. "Get up", I said frantically. They slowly started coming out of their weed induced comas. I pulled to the side of the road, turned my flashers on, and popped the hood.

My PrimeCo phone was roaming and couldn't get a signal. We couldn't use the phone and we were 3 young black men on the side of the road. I figured no one would pull over but after an hour a white man pulled over and offered help. He took both June and Bro to the nearest town to call a tow truck. I was left alone with the truck. After a few hours, a tow truck pulled up behind the truck and I saw June and Bro in the cab. The man looked under the hood of my truck and told me I blew the engine. The pop I heard was a rod going through the bottom of my engine. My truck was placed on the flat bed tow truck and the 4 of us got into the cab.

We were an hour and 15 minutes outside of Gary. He gave me a quote for driving us all the way back to the G, and I agreed before checking my bank account. My phone was roaming and not working. As soon as I got back into my cellular coverage area I called my bank to see how much I had. I'd been spending heavy and it was almost all gone. He pulled the truck into Playboys driveway and parked it. I didn't have a ride so the tow truck driver took me to the bank. He charged me the last $300 I had left in my account. He took me back to Playboys house and dropped me off. I was broke, my truck was broke, and I didn't have a ride home.

I got on my hustle as soon as I got home. I had spent every dime I received from the insurance policy. I found a sucker in MC to buy the broken .22 revolver for $250. I felt bad about it but I didn't care. That was enough to get me a quarter pound of bud for sale.

I started selling and saving. I saved up enough money within 3 months to get a new engine for the Black Blazer. I found a mechanic. I found an engine. I got a U-Haul truck with a car tow on the back. I drove the U-Haul to the junk yard to pick up the used engine.

They fork lifted it into the back. I then went to Playboy's house to get the Black Blazer. It took 4 of us to push it up the ramp but we got it up there. Then I drove to the shop in MC. They took the truck and the engine and told me to give them a week.

A week was all it took and I was back on the road. I knew then I had to hustle to make money. When I had the insurance money I never thought it would run out. I thought I could just keep spending and it would magically reappear. I knew different now and I was more determined than ever to get my grind on.

I had gotten my truck fixed and weed sales were good. I was able to convince one of the geekers in the G to buy me a new pistol in his name. I got a .45mm Ruger. I learned that I wasn't the smartest hustler when I got my first pound of weed.

Notorious

Moms came home early one evening when I was in the middle of bagging up dime and quarter bags of bud. I gathered all my paraphernalia and went to the Black Blazer. I laid my baggies out for stuffing. I had my scale on the armrest and the pound between my feet.

My truck was backed into the parking space so I could see the street and any cars moving through or pass. The sun was down and it was dark outside. The street light across the parking lot cast a dim light into my truck. I turned on the overhead light inside the truck and began bagging up. I had my music on but not loud. I rolled a blunt and zoned out as I bagged up the weed in the truck.

Bang, Bang, Bang, on the driver's window. I was so engrossed in what I was doing I never bother to look around every few seconds. As I began to look to my left I caught a glimpse of all the illegal activity going on in my truck. Under the light I saw weed, bagged and tagged for sale sitting next to a scale.

Blunt smoke in the air. A big gun tucking into the seat and a large bag of weed between my feet. I focused in and it was moms.

Moms told me she had been standing there for quite some time watching my dumbass bag up weed in a truck under the street light. She made me feel stupid as I should have. She didn't make a scene but let me know I was fucking up. "What if someone else walked up on you", she asked?

She might not have been the only one watching me. I gathered everything in my truck that would have gotten me a case and went into the apartment. Moms never really said much about that afterwards, to be honest nothing else needed to be said.

My grandmother had gotten sick and moms decided we'd move back to the G, so she could take care of her mother. Grandma died a few weeks before we moved. Grandma was my heart. She always looked out for me even more so than her other grandkids. I saw it and I knew she favored me.

After grandma died, our family never got together like we used to when she was alive. I miss those holidays where all my cousins, aunts, and uncles would come together. Grandma left the house to 3 of her daughters. Two of my aunts were in their own homes so my mother and I got Grandma's house.

I was back on the block and ready to make a name for myself in the streets of the G. I'd been grinding on my own for so long I was ready to get into making some real money. Dope money!

Lil Daddy was the only person I knew who was connected to my brother's murder other than Twan. Bro had a weed spot on 41st Ave. It was a large brown brick apartment complex. It was kitty corner from the fire station a block or two west of Broadway. One night I was dropping Bro off at his spot. I pulled up on the corner and he got out the backseat. June was riding shotgun. There were a few people standing on the corner and I didn't pay them much attention. As soon as the door closed Bro came back to the passenger window which was tinted black. June rolled the window down and Bro said "Das, I know you see Lil Daddy. Don't burn up my spot but if you got to you got to!" Bro walked away and June rolled the window back up.

I pulled the blue steel .45 caliber Ruger from under my leg and pointed it at the back of Lil Daddy's head from behind the tint. I had a point-blank shot. I cocked the hammer back. June sat up in his seat and used his whole body to block the window. June pleaded with me not to kill Lil Daddy. He didn't want me to go down that route and for a second I heard his plea. Then, I thought he was scared. The next thought that raced through my head was, he is going to tell on you if you do this right here right now. I was shitty for a while that he didn't let me kill that nigga that night but as I got older I learned to appreciate what he did for me. This wouldn't be the last time June stopped me from killing a nigga. Thank you my nigga!

Being in Gary always felt like a free for all to me. Rules were nonexistent. What mattered was respect and being able to hold down your section and your people. We freely sold dope in the neighborhood. It started in the cul-de-sac.

All the OG's had geekers and there were whole families of dope fiends around the hood we'd sell to. We'd fight for crumbs at first then the OG's started selling us weight. That's when the money started coming in for us all. We'd sit in the circle all night selling dope and smoking bud.

One day I was in the Blazer with Baldy and Playboy. The Blazer was banging my 2 12'speakers in the back and we were feeling the zone. Smoke was in the air as we hot boxed on a regular. We had 3 blunts rolled up and 1 in the air. I had my Ruger 45 cal. and Baldy had his Ruger .9mm this day. In the cut was and old head washing a car. A neighbor wanting some free dope brought me some BBQ that I'd been smelling for a few hours now. We make the transaction he goes on his way with his dope and I got a plate of BBQ. I was smoking so I put the BBQ to the side, wrapped in aluminum foil.

The circle was the cul-de-sac and it sat behind the houses so we had a 360 view of our surroundings. We'd see everything coming before it got to us as we were hidden behind the houses but could view the street clearly. We'd sit there all day and night waiting for the geekers to show up to make a few hits. I had a low spot in the Blazer where I would hide my dope behind the horn. By pure chance I popped the horn off one day and noticed a large cavity where I could stash my shit. I'd keep some dope in the stash at all times; you never know when the money flows.

Police drove up 16th Ave. From our view point we could see them coming and I panicked. We had dope, weed, and guns. Shit! I didn't have a gun permit but Baldy did.

I jumped out the Blazer and grabbed my foil covered BBQ. Baldy jumped out. Playboy stayed in the backseat. I ran to the storage shelter, pass the old head washing the car in the cut. Yanked open the rusted metal door barely on the hinges and closed it behind me. I could hear the police pull up and pull playboy out the truck.

In all the rush I left my gun in the holder on the door. There were also 3 rolled blunts sitting in the ash tray. Why didn't Playboy get out the truck? Why'd he sit there? I could hear the police ask him "is this your truck. Where's the owner?" Playboy said it wasn't his truck and he didn't know where the owner was. I could hear another car pull up. It started to get dark as the red and blue lights begin to light up the back of the brick homes I could see through the slit in the door.

"We got 2 guns!" I could hear in the background. "We got weed!" Damn, this is fucked! I heard the crunch of the dead grass and dirt coming up the cut. "Where's the driver of that truck?" There was a pause and in a low scratchy voice "Ah… he's in there." What the fuck! Did he just tell on me! GOT DAMN IT! Footsteps crunched closer. The metallic grind of rusted metal screech as the door opened. I grabbed my BBQ, opened the foil, and took a bite. As I sat in the dark shed eating my BBQ the officer asked me "What are you doing?" I told him I was eating my BBQ. He pulled me out the shed and led me back to my truck. "Is that your truck?" I told him, yes. "Are those your guns?" I told him, no. "Do you have a permit for those guns?" I told him, no. "Is that your weed?" I told him, no. The officer handcuffed me and sat me next to Playboy on the curb. He pulled the perfectly rolled blunts out and stomped them into the ground. He told me that wouldn't matter because I was going to jail for the guns.

The tow truck pulled up and lifted my Blazer in the air and pulled it away. The police were nice enough to let me see my truck go to jail too. There was still about an 8 ball of bagged up dope in my steering wheel. Damn! If they find that I'm really fucked. I get thrown in the back of the police car in time to see moms walking up through the cut. Here we go again. I'm going to jail again.

The drive to the station always puts things in perspective for me. Thoughts run around your mind like I wish I would of, could of, and should have done something differently. Why didn't Baldy claim the guns? He has a gun permit, right? I got to stop fucking with lames.

I'm 18 and I will be going to the county. I had never been further than a holding cell. It was about to be time for me to really see what I'm made of. I get booked into the station and placed in a cell. Within about an hour or so I was called. "Lord, you made bail" is what I was told. I got a card with a court date and was led to the entrance.

Standing in the lobby was moms and auntie. I'll be damn! She came and got me! I was truly surprised because of all the disappointments I have put her through she actually got me out of jail. She greeted me with a hug. We walked out the door and she asked me "Why did you have 2 guns, D?" She didn't know one of them wasn't mine. All I could say was "Them niggas that killed Ralph is still out here. They tried to get on my trail too. I'm going to kill one of them boys, ma!" Nothing more was ever spoken about that incident.

I've never been dumb. In my head was a need to get my gun permit before I had to go to court. That's exactly what I did. I submitted the paper work to the police station with finger prints. In 2 months, I had my gun permit and it came in time for me to go to court. When I got to court for my gun charge I presented my gun permit to the judge. My case was dismissed. That was such a win for me I didn't know how to contain my emotions that I started crying on my drive home. Free! Winning was a good feeling.

I decided it was time to go back to school and get my GED. I had the Blazer squatting on some 13 inch deep dish chrome spokes that my man Mikeo sold to me for the low low. I told my 16th crew I was going back to school and we should all go to get the school stuff over with. None of us had graduated. None of us were making our parents proud as we did nothing but run the streets, sell dope, smoke and drink. They agreed.

The first day to sign up at the alternative school I was accompanied by June, Playboy, and Bro. We were all in school together. I told them I'll pick everybody up every day, smoke one, then go to class. The school was really loose on rules. We could be in class or not the teachers didn't care. I was there for one thing and that was to study up on the GED test so I could pass it. The next week, Bro stopped coming with us. The week after that Playboy stopped coming too.

Demonstration

June and I decided to take a smoke break one afternoon while at school. We left the alternative school on 21st Ave behind Roosevelt HS and I drove east back towards the hood. It was a sunny summer day. My windows were down and the moon roof was popped open. I was feeling good and my nigga and I were about to get high. In my rearview mirror, I see an oversized SUV riding my ass, dipping from curb to curb. June says, "that's Lil Daddy".

Lil Daddy didn't know I started stalking his every move. I know Lil Daddy didn't pull the trigger but anyone affiliated with the people that killed my brother would feel me. You Feel Me? He didn't know it at the time but I was on his ass from the first day I moved back to the G.

I knew where Lil Daddy's spot was on the End. I thought I was low because I'd just ride by with my windows up peeping the scene. What I didn't know was he was peeping me too. I found out the day he got on my trail when June and I went on our smoke break.

Lil Daddy drove a brown and green Ford Bronco. That truck dwarfed my Blazer once it got behind us. All I saw was bumper in my rearview mirror. He started dipping from side to side and bouncing up and down in his seat. The SUV was occupied by 3 other people whom started getting geeked up too.

They started hanging out the windows and sitting on the window seals. Gang signs were being thrown, although we were in the same gang the G is based on hoods. I drove to 20 Block because there is always someone out there but there wasn't anyone this day. I didn't have a gun on me. I started to panic!

I drove up to 21st Ave and back west on the Ave. They were still dipping behind me and yelling something. Gary police were coming up the Ave and saw them and pulled them over. That was close. I knew to never ride again without my gun.

I needed some big heat so I hollered at Nickels and he let me hold the 12-gauge shot gun. June and I were upset and wanted some get back for the shit they did. We went to the liquor store and got a pint of Paul Masson. I rolled up 3 blunts and pulled into the cul-de-sac so we could plot our next move. I told June I was going to kill this nigga. He had to go and today was going to be it for Lil Daddy. We got a good buzz on, I pulled off, and began to stalk my prey.

I rolled up and down every block on the End because he wasn't at his spot, then I saw his SUV parked in the alley. June wanted me to shoot up the SUV but I needed blood. I wanted blood. Fuck that, somebody was going to die tonight. We circled the block about 10 times and I went back to the hood.

We smoked another blunt and had another drink and went back. The SUV was still in the alley we circled the block a few more times and then I saw the brake lights come on the SUV.

I slowly crept up the block giving him enough time to get out the alley but this time I'd be behind him. He popped out the alley I was there; behind him dipping and bouncing in my seat! June had a .38 caliber revolver and I had the gauge. The back window of the Bronco started to come down. Adrenaline began pumping in every cell of my body as I pumped the gauge.

I perched the gage in-between the frame of the window and the side rear view mirror and lined it up with my left hand while I steered with my right hand. BOOM! I shattered the driver's side windows.

The Bronco lost control and went through the gate of somebody's home. I pulled the gauge back in and pumped it. I put it back on its perch, BOOM! The Bronco crashed into the side of a brick home on the corner. I pulled the gauge back in and pumped it. I stopped in the middle of the street and tried to get my barring's. Everyone in the Bronco scattered like roaches when it hit the house. I circled the block looking for stragglers. If I saw one of them they'd be dead. I circled the block again. I saw nothing.

I stopped in the middle of the street again and got out. I told June to drive. I was going to steal his Bronco that they left on the side of the house. I ran through the hole in the gate that they created when they drove through it and hopped in the driver's seat. It was still running. I tried to put the Bronco in gear but quickly learned it was a stick shift and I couldn't drive a stick.

The gears crunched as I tried to take it but the SUV didn't move. I hopped back out and ran back to the street where June was pulling down the block. I jumped up and down waving my arms hoping he'd see me. He did and stopped. I ran up and jumped back in the driver's seat dipped off.

I went right back to the cul-de-sac where we were met by a few OG's. We proudly told the story of how I chopped they shit down and had them running. Since this was my first demonstration in the G since I've been back I was super geeked up and ready for war. "You got to go. You can't be around here. Get low for a few weeks" OG instructed me to move around until the heat died. Calls started coming in from my niggas letting me know they'd seen the demonstration I put down in the hood. "You got to go!"

I heard enough so I went back to MC. Latina and I had formed a relationship. I could count on her to be there for me and she was. We stayed at her parents' house in the basement. Calls back to the neighborhood were frequent and long. What was going on, who was looking for me? Would I be safe and who'd hold me down? All those questions were asked as I talked to whomever from the hood would entertain my call. After about a week of me being in MC with Latina I went back to the G.

I needed to finish school so I decided to take my GED test. I had only gone to the alternative school for a month. I only worked on my math and English composition. The other subjects were not that difficult to me. Between banging and going to jail I had a lot going on.

I registered for the GED and I had to go to the Career Center off King Dr. The room was filled with grown people but I didn't care much about what was going on with them. I had heard stories about this test from my peers. None of them had passed the whole thing in one shot before.

The way it worked was you had to have a minimum score on the test to pass and if you didn't pass a part of the test you could retake that part. I think there were about 5 subjects you had to pass. I sat for what I thought would be a long day, but before I knew it, I had finish the test.

For the Love of Money

Once again, I was in need of a gun. I talked the same geeker who bought my first Ruger into buying me another in his name. I had a gun permit but I was still too young to purchase a pistol. You had to be 21 before you could buy your own pistol. It didn't matter. I had money and work.

The combination of money and power made geekers puppets, niggas too. For the right price, anything could be done. I'd seen a lot but when I got my money up, life changed. Men would sell their wives for dope. Son's selling work to their mothers, fathers, uncles, I mean you name it was happening.

I could buy anything on the street. Guns, cars, women, rims, speakers, clothes, shoes, I mean anything. If you were hungry, someone was selling a plate of food somewhere. There was never a shortage of drama either. Someone was always beefing, so I learned to watch the people I hung with because niggas were dying left and right.

I've seen low self-esteem women let niggas molest them in public, behind closed doors too. I've seen some of the most beautiful women let men treat them like a possession. Some women like to be treated like garbage. It's like an addiction to them. If their man for the moment is not beating her, that man is not loving her. That man, her man, is a pussy or somehow less than a "real nigga". I never understood it but I was a nigga too. Who am I to question the game? All I can do is learn.

One night my bud man, Bennie, and I wanted a head doctor to do something strange for some change. The bud man had a super slut in Ivanhoe Projects on the West Side. We called the bitch Slob Master J! Oh! Slob Master J could suck a dick. I never knew who this chick was but if my bud man made the call and set up an appointment, we got serviced.

We'd go inside the small project home and sit on the couch for about 2 minutes or so. Just enough time to spark a blunt and find a seat. She'd lead us back one at a time. I sat on the couch the first time anxious. I was passed the blunt and I hit it hard to shake off my nerves. Bennie came from the back and she stood there like who next. I stood up. She grabbed my hand and led me back to the throne.

The throne was a pile of boxes wedged in between the wall and the washing machine. I took a seat on the boxes and put one arm on the top of the washing machine. She pulled my dick out and kneeled in front of me as if she was about to worship my joint. I couldn't see a thing. It was pitch black on the throne.

I pulled her tits out and slid her pants down as she sucked harder. I finished in her mouth. I gathered myself and went back to the living room. I grabbed the blunt and sat on the couch. The bud man got led back to the throne.

Bennie and I started laughing and shaking hands. When it was all over we just left. I didn't even say thank you.

I've seen the emasculation of our men too. At the other end of the spectrum there are men who will not work or hustle. These men sit at home doing nothing but take. They take food out of the mouths of the children of the women they are living with. They take money out of their girlfriend's pocket by spending, asking, always needing.

They suck the life out of the home and the people they are around. The men who are good at this trick will make you depend on them or be afraid of them. They offer nothing but dick and for some women that's a good enough role model for their children. They give good dick and now he lives with you and doesn't contribute anything else.

I've given money to my niggas to entertain me. One night we were all high, drunk and bored. It was about 2 in the morning. We were sitting in front of Playboys house in the Black Blazer. We were 4 deep that night. I asked one of them to pull his draws off, put it on his head, grab his dick, and run to the end of the next block screaming "I got my balls in my hand" butt ass naked!

We sat in the truck haggling prices for a while which really made it funny. I think it started with him just running down the street screaming. As he up the ante I upped the consequence. In the end, we agreed on $100. He had to be screaming at the top of his lungs. Underwear on his head. Ass naked. Dick in his hand and he had to walk.

As my nigga prepared to take his early morning stroll we all were dying laughing. He started out of the drive way. I started the truck and followed him. I turned my high beam lights on and off as I made them flicker behind him. I turned the beat up to full throb at 2AM. Mystikal screamed out the speakers "the man right ch'ere"! I began honking the horn.

We were laughing so hard my stomach began hurting. "Slow down you walking too fast", I tried to speak but my full belly laugh made it difficult. HONK! HONK! Flicker, flicker. He walked screaming "I got my balls in my hand"! We were in the truck gasping for air and talking shit. To the end of the block and back he walked in his white sock feet. I tried to wake up everyone in the neighborhood if I could. That was one of the funniest things I've done with dope money. I paid my nigga and we laughed about that for months.

We hugged the block like our lover on a daily basis. I'd wake up in the morning roll a blunt, find the perfect song, and start bending blocks. As I smoked, I drove around the East Side looking for geekers. They'd be out hustling trying to find some money to give to the dope man, me. The female geekers would always have some money from sucking dick or fucking some dude.

Sometimes if I was feeling a certain kind of way I'd look for them to suck my dick too. I could give them less than a nickel sack and they'd get me off early in the morning. They would say, "I need a wake up" and after they took this nut I would wake them up with a pinch of work. I liked getting the geekers early in the morning because if you had good work, they would call you all day long. I learned the game. I was hungry and I was going to get it.

Time to Fly

Moms got tired of seeing me do nothing all day and night. She gave me an ultimatum. Go to school, go to work, or get out of her house. Moms always stood on her word and I should have known this by 18 but I called her bluff. Within a week of her statement to me, she took my house key away and gave me a curfew.

She let me know I had to leave her house when she had to go to work. I needed to be in the house by midnight if I wanted to sleep there because she was not opening the door after that. Moms worked a schedule that was all over the place. Some mornings she had to be out by 6 in the morning. Some nights she didn't get home until 10 PM. The first morning she woke me up, shit got real!

It was an early morning and she was up around 5 AM. I could hear her stirring around the house and I played like I was in deep sleep. She hollered my name and I rolled over. She bust the door to my room open and screamed at me to "Get up" and I did. I was in my truck at 5:30. It was chilly and frost covered my windshield. Thick, almost mystic, silver colored dew covered the grass. Spider webs were visible as their geometry appeared to be outlined in thousands of tiny bubbles of dew. I could see my breath as I started the engine. I rolled a blunt as my truck warmed. Thoughts raced and collided in my head, what will I do now? As the sun grew in the sky so did my awareness, my high, and the temperature. I will do what I do best... grind, find geekers and sell this work.

I was upset because I had to leave my home when my moms went to work. That anger gave way to me enjoying the fact that I was the only nigga on the block with work. I was up in the morning hours before the other dope boys came out to get their day started. I would ride pass the dope spots and filter off the fiends before they knock on the door to get some work. I was buying more dope than ever. I was getting ounces now instead of 16ths and 8 balls. I was bagging up thousands of dollars' worth of work.

I was buying a new outfit every week just because I could. New music was a must as well. I kept the beat banging and that was my announcement to the geekers I was coming. I'd be rolling around at 6 in the morning rattling the windows and walls of all the houses I passed. I didn't care. Car alarms would go off as I passed by blaring my music and geekers would flag me down. I loved my life.

Thanks moms, you took my hustle to the next level and this was truly an unintended benefit to the consequences she thought had been put on me.

I had my gun confiscated and I was without a gun for a short time. I got my money right I went and bought another .45 Caliber Ruger. I was back and I found Lil Daddy's new spot too. I began terrorizing him almost on a daily basis. Hell, I'd go fuck with him when I got bored.

He and his boys got a spot on the End and they would be out there deep, at first. When I first rolled up on him it was the middle of the day. June and I had finished smoking a blunt while driving around the East Side. I always like stroking the End because there are always geekers down there. I bent a block and saw a bunch of niggas outside a multiple story red brick house with the steps extended to the street. I slowed down just to get a good look at who was out there. I saw Lil Daddy.

I rolled around the block and told June I was about to chop at all them niggas. If he wasn't down, I'd take him back to the hood. June shrugged his shoulders as if he didn't give a fuck. My drive around the block was to get my nerves together. I rolled back to the street they were on and could see 5 people, all males. Twan was there with Lil Daddy.

My window came down to expose my pistol. I opened fire! I unloaded the clip. They spread out like butter. All we saw was elbows and assholes. I locked onto Lil Daddy. I changed the clip in my pistol and tried to catch him. That bitch ass nigga is fast and slippery like the snake he is.

Bending blocks and dipping through alleys I kicked up dirt and rocks. My tires were screeching as I revved the engine and the tires fought with the street. With my body, halfway out the window, I shot at him with my left and steered with the right hand. I didn't catch him this time.

I liked it. All these niggas some bitches. That shit made my dick hard like in New Jack City. We rolled back to the hood and laughed off the shit we did. It got to a point that we'd bomb on the enemy in broad daylight or just on site. There were no rules and we played the odds.

In the G, chances were you could have a conversation with the police about a crime you'd just committed and they'd be none the wiser. No one cared and in the circle of people I was with, no one gave a fuck. Play your role and don't be extra to gain attention. The real killers are the calmest people I know, until they are not calm anymore. Most of these so call hard niggas were bitches.

I was out here and dabbling in anything that would get me paid. I was on moms schedule for about 2 months when I got the results in the mail for my GED. I had passed! Not only did I pass but I did so well they gave me a half scholarship to Calumet College of St. Joseph. Awe shit! This was my ticket back in the house.

I told moms. I don't think I'd ever seen her eyes smile before, until that day. She was truly proud of me. Thinking about that day now brings tears to my eyes. She was happy that something she said to me throughout the years stuck in my head. I was relieved that I wasn't a failure. It's an epiphany to know you can. I had been conditioned by my peers and my environment to believe I was no better than a criminal. I gained a piece of self-esteem back with that letter. I got my key to the house back and my outlook on life was different.

College

College started the fall of 1999. I had never been enthusiastic about school and I hated high school with a passion, but something was different, I wanted to be in school. It took me away from the hood and the craziness I was dealing with daily. I would go to school in the mornings and be home by 4pm. That was cool because I kept the grind going.

After school, I would post up in the hood and do my homework in my truck while waiting for my phone to ring or for someone to walk up to get some work. It was working for me until the niggas in the circle got to tripping. I was getting money. I still fucked with my 16th crew on a daily.

Baldy and OG started getting mad because all the geekers were coming to me. I was band from the circle. I was told not to come over there anymore. I was hurt to my core but it didn't stop anything, I still got money every day; moms stayed on the Ave. All the geekers had to pass moms' house to get to the circle. So, I started posting up in moms' driveway. Studying and selling work.

Without my knowledge at the time; what had happened was I had instilled a work ethic, self-motivation, and follow through. I learned it all from the game and my drive to get money.

Although I was moving forward and trying to become a better person I was still in the hood. Hood niggas only understand hood shit. I was confusing the niggas I bust guns with and sold dope with. They couldn't understand why I had wanted to work for the "white man". I was filled with doubt about how I wouldn't graduate because I was told, the "white man" won't let me get a degree.

None of the people I grew up with had gotten their GED let alone went to college. They would make fun about how I would be sitting in the truck studying and selling dope. They couldn't understand I wanted to do something different than what we were doing.

I felt as if I were being pulled between two worlds. The everyday struggle of trying to be the best student I could versus wanting to fit into my environment and be hood. I was hood. I had shot at Lil Daddy so much that when I'd pull down on the End I would start seeing niggas running. Streaks of colors would be all I could see as niggas cleared the block in fear I'd start shooting. Half the time I wasn't even looking for him. I would be bending blocks to make a few hits and get some money. It was still hilarious because I made them niggas track stars.

I figured I wouldn't have to worry about Lil Daddy trying to chase me anymore. He was a bitch nigga and he knew where we stood. I was a problem and he knew it. He couldn't stop it and my determination was stronger. I didn't give a fuck and I'd kill to prove it.

I got a call from my up north Cuzzo, Puc. Puc and I are the closest in age and mentality of my cousins. At this time, he was living in North Chicago and he knew I had the plug on everything. It was a drought on weed where he was and he needed the plug. He told me his guy needed a pound of bud. I told him what the ticket was and come through. No worries.

His guy agreed to the price and they headed down the highway to the G. Before Puc left the city, I told him my rules. #1 when I get you the pound, put it up. #2 pay me my dues up front if you are good with the pound. #3 drop me off and go straight home.

Things went left as soon as he pulled up to my moms' house. I was under the impression that it would just be him and his boy. When I looked into the car I noticed 3 people. I wasn't comfortable riding to the spot 4 deep but I did it anyway. We pulled up to the spot. I hopped out and hollered at my man. I looked at a few pounds and picked the one with the best looking fluffy buds, with a good scent, and little to no seeds at the bottom. I paid my man and went back to the car.

I let Puc's man look at the pillow to see if this was what he wanted. He agreed and broke me off my middle man fee. Then Cuzzo broke rule #1. His man put the bud in his pants. That's not putting it up.

We pulled off on our way back to the hood to drop me off. We made a left and was on 20th Ave. We made the next left and we were on Georgia St. riding pass the middle school. Coming up the block was a County Police car. As we passed each other all three of these dumbasses turn their head to the left to look at the passing police. My heart dropped in my stomach because I knew what they had just done would get us stopped.

Without missing a beat as our back bumper passed the polices back bumper, the police hit their break lights. Fuck! We turned right on 17th Ave., by that time the police had completely turned around. We turned left on Rhode Island and the police lit up the berries.

I was in the back seat behind the passenger, his man. Cuzzo rolled the window down as the police approached. Before the police could say anything, his man started wigging out. "What the fuck you pull us over for! We ain't did shit", he shouted guilty.

The police bent down to see the passenger clearly. "Calm down sir. I'm not talking to you", said the police.

"This some bullshit. We ain't did nothing". Cuzzo started getting amped up too. I put my hand on his shoulder and shook my head, no. He calmed down as his man gassed up.

His man started bouncing in his seat and jerking his body as he protested us being pulled over. I told Cuzzo, "Your man's about to go to jail if he doesn't calm down. Don't you say anything unless you are asked", I told Cuzzo. "I care about you. I don't even know these niggas".

Backup was called and as we sat in the middle of the block we were surrounded by 5 different County Police cars. They all had their lights on and flashing the whole block. We had become a spectacle as I noticed the neighbors coming out of their homes to witness what was happening. Once the police felt secure they ordered all of us out of the car with our hands in the air. His man lost it. Hollering and screaming at the police, they ordered him to the ground. At gun point he was handcuffed and led back to one of the police cars.

They began to pat him down and he continued to lose his shit. "I think I found the problem", one of the police shouted. He held up a fluffy pound of bud. They continued the pat down and they found another big bag of weed. I was confused when I saw the other bag. It was like a half pound.

Who goes out of state to get some product and brings product with them? This had to be one of the dumbest situations I'd ever been in, who was this ass backwards hustler? Why was he so belligerent? Why did they all look at the police when we passed them? All this was running through my head when I gave Cuzzo the look. All he had to do was be cool.

They searched the car, searched us, and found nothing. His mans was taken to the county jail in Crown Point, IN. I went home. I told Cuzzo to go home. They rolled out and I thought that was the end of it but I was wrong.

About an hour later as I was sitting back telling my niggas the story and smoking a blunt when my phone rang. It was Cuzzo. He wanted the information on how to get his man out of jail. I gave him the info he needed then I heard "Awe shit", over the phone. "What's good Cuzzo? You good"? "I'm being pulled over by the State Police"! Wow, Cuzzo couldn't catch a break. He got off the phone. He made it home. Never bring drugs to a drug deal, is the moral of that story.

KD

The Circle City Classic was the thing to do when it came around every year. I think it is some kind of college football game. I have no idea really. I did know all the bad bitches from all around would go to it. All the balling ass niggas would go to get at the hoes.

It was more of a dope boy convention. I had rims, a truck, and speakers. I was ready to go and be seen. We rolled out from the hood in a 4 car caravan heading down 65 south.

I was trying to get in a player mood and had the SWV beating most of the trip. We didn't make any plans other than we were going. Smoking and swerving down the highway we made it to downtown Indy. We went in and out of all the hotels we checked but they were all booked.

We were a few blocks from downtown and we found a seedy low budget motel that had a few rooms left. We pooled our money and the 8 of us rented 2 adjoining rooms. The parking lot was busy. Big rims of chrome and gold matched the grills on the front of the cars they adorned. Music shook the earth from every direction.

The niggas had on new crispy outfits and shoes. The women wore the skimpiest of clothes. Tits barely being held in their shirts shook with every step. Ass bottoms were hanging underneath tightly fitting shorts, skirts, and what looked like panties. Oh my God! This is the shit, I thought. There were bitches everywhere.

We opened the door to the adjoining rooms and began smoking weed and plotting the next move. Nickels brought a half pound of bud with him. He left the room to scope the halls. Shortly he came back and started bagging up bud. He was selling dime bags for $20.

Knocks on the door were coming back to back as people got the word that good weed was on deck. He sold all but an ounce that we later smoked. I got a call from my nigga KD. I hadn't seen him since I moved out of MC. He'd gone into the military and was out on leave.

KD had been through military training and had put on some solid pounds. He bought a new purple Chevy Monte Carlo. It was sitting on 20 inch chrome skates. He had the first pair of spinners I had seen and was able to touch. I spun them around a few times, posted up outside his car, and politicked for a minute. We were hollering at all of the women that were passing, trying to get a number or maybe get them back up to my room. KD told me he'd gotten married. That took me by surprise.

KD had brought one of his homeboys with him and they had their own mission. I shook his hand and they left. That was the last time I saw KD. The very next year after the Super Bowl he went into the garage of his wife's home and killed himself.

I never knew what happened for sure but there were rumors about his wife cheating and others about the Iraqi war. What I do know is, I never knew he felt so bad and I wish I could have helped him. I wish I'd never smoked weed with him and had him skipping school. I wished I had never instigated the fight in the bowling alley for him to go to juvenile detention. KD was a jock before he met me and because of me, he had to drop out of school and go to Job Corp.

I've never forgiven myself for what happened to him. Because of KD's death positive energy is the only thing I can give to others now. I will never again show, encourage, or teach others the "hood" side of life. I can give growth and understanding of how we should represent ourselves. I can paint a beautiful picture of my struggle to success through my own perspective of my life and times. These days my positivity radiates off of me like the sun on human flesh in the summer.

Everything we needed was in the room while at the Circle City Classic. Liquor, weed, and the girls were up and down the hallway. We were enjoying the night. A knock on the door got the attention of the room. The door was answered to reveal a thick chocolate woman wearing panties and a bra, stepping through the doorway.

With the confidence of a model, she had one hand on her hip. The bottom of her buttocks peaked out her panties. Her lips puckered out when she asked, "how many niggas were in the room"? We told her 4. She looked around and took a mental note of all the faces. She said, "wait a minute I'll be right back", she turned around and walked out the room, all I saw was ass.

We looked at each other puzzled in anticipation of what she was coming back to do. Anticipation grew. Was she getting some more big booty bitches? Why'd she leave?

When she returned to the room she came back with 3 other women. They were all half naked. They were all stunning. One was dark chocolate thick and short. She had on red heels to match her lipstick.

One was milk chocolate and taller than the others. She came in the room first. One was a redbone with a perfect waist to ass ratio. She was the star of the group. Redbone got to shaking ass and showing pussy to the room full of horny and intoxicated men.

She got on the bed simulating riding a dick. She was bouncing and jiggling. Her ass had waves, looking like the ocean, rippling up and down her booty cheeks as she gyrated. I mean, DAMN! It was on!

The taller chocolate one spoke up again and said, "what yall got? $50 for head $100 to fuck"! Niggas started digging in their pockets, turning their backs, and peeling through the wads of drug money. The flick of paper scraped as money was counted by all men in the room.

The air was cloudy, full of weed smoke and pheromones. Naked, sweaty women waited to be paid. The first woman was chosen, like a bad auction. We opened the door to the next room so they could get in on the action too. When I looked around everyone was getting sucked and fucked. Moans bounced off other moans. Bodies smashed. Ass was everywhere. Everyone got off that night and it was awesome!

No one really cared about money. I could spend $500 in a day on clothes and music. By the end of the night I'd have that $500 back, plus more. I bought a new outfit every week for $100 to $300 per outfit. I had leather outfits, suede outfits, limited edition only 2 of these came to the city outfits.

The grind was a must. I'd wake up in the morning wash my ass and grab my keys. Out the door and into the Black Blazer. Pop off my horn, the low spot, where I kept my work and weed. Grab the bud. Break it down. Roll up a blunt, put the truck in gear and bend a few blocks beating my music.

I'd find some geekers and flag them down. If they nodded their head, I pulled over and let them get in the truck. I'd bend a block while serving them what they needed. Then I'd drop them off where I picked them up and I would continue bending blocks looking for geekers to serve.

After making a few mobile hits I would pull up in the Circle or on 20 block and post up waiting to make more hits. Dope sold itself. The trick to getting money back then was to be accessible, have fat sacks, and good work for the geekers to smoke.

Everyone I knew sold something or smoked something. No one had a job other than the hustle. I had a work ethic. I'd give all the geekers my pager number after a hit. I was recruiting geekers from every spot I hustled. I'd tell them to page me with their number and how much work they wanted behind the number.

I might get a page that looked like 555-1234-50. That means they wanted $50 worth of work. I'd call them back and be on my way faster than any of the other dope boys. I was hungry for that money. Selling dope was just as addictive as the dope being sold.

I needed to get the money. I could do whatever I wanted, whenever I wanted. I smoked the fattest blunts. Drove the hottest cars on the street. Affiliated with some bad motherfuckers from the Valley to the Block.

I had access to whatever I needed from guns, to girls, to drugs. My niggas were riding candy paint and large inch rims. We turned heads wherever we went. We turned out clubs, shot up blocks, and raced our cars like they were rentals. We fought pit bulls in backyards and in basements for money to relax. Nothing mattered but the day you were living.

It had been years since I'd shot at Twan. June, Playboy and I were at Carolina Park one afternoon sitting in the Blazer smoking a blunt. We had parked under the big shade tree and chilled getting high. Twan couldn't have been paying attention this day as he walked home. He came across the street and walked directly pass the front of my truck focused on his mission.

Maybe he didn't see me but I saw him. I grabbed my Ruger and pulled the hammer back. I asked June for his revolver and he gave it to me. I jumped out the truck and yelled "Twan" with both pistols pointed at his head. He looked up and froze in place.

I then noticed the 30 round extended clip showing from his back pocket. He instantly started bitching up. "I didn't have nothing to do with Ralph getting killed. Ralph was my man. It wasn't me. You want Lil Daddy I can set him up for you!"

My blood boiled. My eyes bulged out of their sockets and my heart pumped hard as I walked up to Twan. "I don't need your help nigga! Just like I got your ass I'll get him too!" He never moved as he begged. I put the Ruger to the side of his head and Twan started crying. "Please don't kill me"! I looked over at June.

For the second time in my life, June saved my life. June looked more afraid than Twan and he didn't have a gun pointed at his head. He stood to the side of Twan, just close enough to get in my peripheral view, and slowly shook his head. He was telling me, no. I looked at Playboy and I saw nothing in his eyes. I looked back at June. June wasn't ready for this. Once again, I thought to myself if you do this, you'll have to kill him too. I sent Twan on his way.

Killing Twan was not for me to do. However, I do regret not taking his chopper. I was so caught in the moment I sent him on his way without even a smack to the face with the pistol. I watched him walk away never looking back or reaching for his gun.

He knew I held his life in my hands. He never knew I shot at him with Chris back in the day but he knew right here and now that I could have parted him from this world. That's power. Being a manager and telling your staff what to do is not power. Holding the balance of life and death in your hand is power. Having a crackhead do whatever you want for some crack is power. Having someone do whatever you want for money is power. Having so much love or loyalty that someone would rob, kill, or steal for you is power. I never saw Twan again, but I heard he was later murdered.

I guess niggas was tired of getting ran off the End when I rolled through there. I was paid a visit one afternoon while chilling in Playboy's driveway. The buzz in the street was loud about some nigga getting out of jail. I had heard he used to rob one of the OG's in the hood back in the day on a regular basis.

I guess one of his people was tired of running from me so when Stafford got out of jail he and Dirty Ant pulled up and blocked off the driveway where Playboy and I were sitting. Just so happens this is one of the days I'd left my Ruger in the house. They got out the car and walked up the driveway to the driver's side door. I had a brick looking Prime Co phone at the time. I waited until they got just close enough to see me take something and put it under my leg.

I didn't know the nigga and I feared no nigga. When he asked if I knew who he was I said, "No." He let me know that Dirty Ant was his man and if I fucks with his man I'm fucking with him. He said his peace and because I'm sure he thought I put a pistol under my leg he made it short. They walked back to the car and peeled off with a screech.

I just so happened to be rolling through the hood one day when I noticed a moving truck in front of a green house. I saw an old man and Dirty Ant moving a table to the truck. Look at this shit here, I thought to myself. I turned around and parked in front of the house. The old man came out the door and I told him to send Dirty Ant out the house.

I pulled my pistol out and let my arm dangle out the window. The old man went in the house and Dirty Ant appeared in the doorway. The door was closed behind him. I pointed the Ruger at Dirty Ant as he was still in the door frame. He pressed and jiggled the door knob but to no reprieve.

I never said a word as I pointed the pistol. He tried to press himself through the cracks in the door. "I didn't know he had something to do with killing your brother. I didn't know. I'm not with that." I just stared at him with my pistol pointed at his face from my truck sitting in the street. He pressed into the frame as if to become one with the wood. "I'll help you get Lil Daddy" he pleaded. I thought to myself damn would I turn on my nigga?

Lil Daddy's boys would give him up in a minute. All these niggas are bitches, all of them. I opened my mouth for the first time. "You KNOW don't you?" I stared at him. "You KNOW, right?" He shook his head, yes. "You know I could kill you right now, right!" he shook his head and said "Yes!" I pulled off and went back to the hood to tell the niggas about what just happened. I never had another problem out of Dirty Ant.

The universe works in mysterious ways and I have been a witness to how things are in works without your knowledge. My chosen field of study was psychology. Curiosity of the behaviors of people had been a consistent line of thought as I traveled through the many situations I had found myself. Why had I been in situations that made me a better man but left others in the same situation lost? How could your perspective be so different when we experience the same occurrence? My Blazer broke down around my sophomore year of college.

My moms managed a department store in MC. She had a blue Ford Contour, that was her first car. She had bought it right before we moved back to the G. When I started going to college her trust in me grew. She would let me drive the car to school depending on my schedule or she would drop me off and pick me up later. It led to long hours at school. I would be at school at 8 in the morning and on most nights, not leave school until 10 in the evening.

College came natural as my desire to learn was stronger than I knew. I didn't mind the long hours at school because I was really into the knowledge I was gaining as well as the different kinds of people I was meeting. My face became known and I was asked to take part in a new program the college was offering. They wanted to help new students transition in to the college atmosphere better, so they wanted all the newbies to have mentors.

As a mentor, I would turn the new students on to the different experiences the school had to offer and help them when needed. A friend that supported you is basically what I was. I also got a discount on my tuition. I became a member of the college and I enjoyed what I did too. The school was also growing. They started a basketball team. I was asked to be mentors to all the males on the basketball team their inaugural year.

By my sophomore year in college, I was 6 feet 8 inches and I was cleaner cut than I had ever been in my life. I had cut my braids off when I got my GED. I got glasses my freshman year of college because the words kept moving around on the pages of the books I was reading. I took learning seriously and how could I not when I was at school for 10 hours a day, 3 days a week?

I would have my stash of weed rolled in joints that I would keep in my pack of squares. I'd walk around the outside of the school and smoke a joint, then go back in and study. I never attended one day of college sober, no one ever knew or suspected a thing. I was making the dean's list consistently. I was showing and proving.

I enjoyed all of my psychology classes and I took them seriously. I asked questions and I was truly interested in the subject matter. I'd had 2 classes with Ms. Butcher, one of my psychology professors, before she stopped me after class. "Do you have a job?" she asked me. I didn't so I told her "No."

She told me to apply at the School City of Hammond for a job as a Behavioral Interventionist. She explained that the job was on a grant and she thought I might be a good fit. I did as she instructed, and I was surprised when I actually got a call for a phone interview. The phone interview went well, and I was asked to come in for an in-person interview in front of the board. I was nervous, but I was ready.

I ironed out a blue button up shirt and some brown slacks. I wasn't comfortable in the clothes, but moms said I looked good. When I was called into the room for my interview I was confident but afraid when I looked upon 14 pairs of eyes staring at me. None of the people in the room look like me. They were all white.

I did recognize one face in the room. It was Ms. Butcher. I had no idea she'd be on the hiring board. I sat in front of the seven people and composed myself and my thoughts. I answered every question with articulate responses. I never let a slang word come out of my mouth. I did what I was supposed to do because I had the job before I left the room. Thank you, Ms. Butcher, for seeing something in me that no one had seen in me before you opened the door. I told you I'd make you proud for helping me get my first real job!

I was working and at this time in my life I stopped selling dope. I was working for 2 elementary schools and I didn't want to be in the paper for something stupid like getting caught with dope. Since I had reliable income I was able to convince moms to cosign on a new truck for me.

We went down to the car lot and I picked a 4-door forest green 1998 Chevy Blazer. It had a sun roof and grey leather seats. I took it right to the sound shop and fitted it with two 15 inch subwoofers, a battery capacitor to store voltage, and a amp to pump the bass. I also put green lights in the chrome windshield washer nozzles that stuck out the top of the hood. The last trick I put on it was a strobe light in my headlights that beamed green. I liked it. It was mine.

The hood was good. Everywhere I went throughout the East Side, my niggas was getting money. I really focused on dumping at Lil Daddy but when I got the green truck I slowed down fucking with him. We were riding 4 deep in the truck one night when my whole outlook on thug life changed.

I considered my Blazer semi luxury. I mean it wasn't a Lexus but it had leather and beat. I was riding with Nickels, Smoke, and Snoop. The sun was going down and we ended up riding through Marshall Town. Nickels was my man.

I didn't really fuck with Smoke and Snoop like that but they were Nickels boys and they'd never crossed me. They were cool, just not my niggas. We turned into old Marshall Town and took the right at the fork in the road, there was a house party. There were 30 people out there crowding around and having a good time.

This part of the G is usually folks heavy. We were a truck full of Vice Lords. From the backseat, I could hear Smoke say "Let's go back around the block and dump on them crabs!" I hadn't even realized that I wasn't the only one strapped in the truck. Then I heard a pistol cock back and the distinctive sound of a bullet being chambered. "Whoa, slow down killa" is all I could get out before this fool stuck his pistol out my back window. "This ain't the demo truck. Let me take yall back to your ride and you can bust all you want at them niggas." "Awe nigga fuck them crabs. Let's go kill all them niggas!"

I could see in my rear view mirror this nigga rubbing his hands together and getting geeked up to mass murder a group of people I didn't know. Yeah it was folks out there but I looked like a family party. "Fuck that shit go back, Das" was demanded from the back seat.

This was the first time in my life I was not interested in getting down for the demonstration. What if those niggas started shooting at us and we get killed? Who is them niggas? Why do they want to kill these people? Who the fuck am I riding with? All these thoughts ran through my head as I tried to navigate the maze of streets that make up old Marshall Town.

I tried my best not to make a wrong turn that would put me back on a path pass the house party. I thought quick and drove even faster as I got back to 21st Ave. "I'm a drop yall off. You can do what you want when you not in my truck." I could hear the sounds of disappointment and anger. I knew they'd go back. I couldn't drop them niggas off fast enough. Snoop was later killed so was Smoke. I never knew if it was retaliation from the Marshall Town demonstration or not.

I was making weekly trips to MC to see Latina. Once I got established I made her more of a focus. She would come to see me in the G whenever she got a chance. We were together every weekend. I was either at her parents' home or she was spending the night at my mom's house.

Latina showed me love. She was always there for me even when I was caught up in the streets or in school. She was the first girlfriend I'd ever had to really treat me like she liked me and not like she wanted something from me. School, work, and Latina kept me busy during those days.

Latina spent the night at my house one weekend and when we awoke it was a beautiful day. It was the first 80-degree day of the year. We needed to eat and I favored the deli sandwich shop in Merrillville. I rolled a 2 blunts, one for trip there and one for the trip back. I fired up the blunt and we took Broadway all the way from 15th Ave to 80th and something Ave.

She got what she wanted from the deli as did I. We jumped back in the truck and I fired up the second blunt. Back down Broadway I had all the windows down as we sucked in the heat from the sun. The warm breeze cuddled my skin like a warm embrace. My music was perfect for the day as I was bumping D'Angelo "Cruising" and loving life.

As we pulled up to the stop light heading North; I saw a green car run the light doing about 70 mph weaving through stopped traffic, going in the opposite direction. Police were pretty far behind him and I was actually geeked to see the bad guy getting away.

I was the first in line as I pulled up to the next red light around 71st Ave. and I hit the blunt. The light turned green and I pulled off grasping the steering wheel with my left hand as I was holding the blunt in my right hand. Before I could comprehend what was going on I heard ear piercing tires screeching. Everything slowed down like in the movies. I looked into my rearview mirror. I saw a green blur. Then I felt a jerk and heard a crash.

We'd just been hit in the rear driver's corner. Since we were moving it was like the police did a "pit" maneuver because the truck spun out of control. I remember spinning the wheel in complete circles and trying to watch out for the cars in the street as I was spinning around. I rotated the wheel as fast as it needed to turn and I kept the truck from flipping.

Then, BAM! The truck stopped. I looked down and then I looked forward. I looked at the steering wheel and then the piece of blunt that I was still holding. I thought to myself "well damn that wasn't too bad". Then I looked over at Latina.

My heart sunk into my stomach as all I could see was the left side of her body. We'd hit a tree and it collapsed the passenger side of the truck. The first thing out of her mouth was "give me the weed. We got to get rid of the weed." I told her not to worry about that. I grabbed my phone and tried to call the police but I was so shook and shaking that I couldn't dial the number. My fingers fumbled over the dial pad. I was telling myself, dial 911 but it didn't translate to action.

She began to say it was hard for her to breathe. I tried to keep it together and dial again. I hopped out the truck to try to get my shit together. My fingers began to work with my brain again. I dialed 911 and I got through to the police. I couldn't explain where I was but the operator told me other people had called and help was on the way. The mind works in weird ways too because I didn't notice that there were about 30 people lining the street. Everyone offering help. I couldn't see the people because I was focused on trying to help Latina.

When I regained my composure, I looked at the truck. The truck became part of the tree as the two melded together. The passenger side was completely crushed in with a gangster lean unfitting for Latina. The roof was leveled to the same height as the hood of the truck. I sat in the truck until help arrived.

I held Latina's hand hoping for the best as she moaned and grunted in sounds of pain. She complained of breathing problems and not being able to move or feel her arms and legs. The firetruck pulled up sirens blaring. The firemen told me to get out the truck and ushered me to the side. A neighbor from the hood happened to be driving by and she got out consoling me. She held me in her breast as I wept.

The firemen placed a golden yellow blanket over Latina's body. What was going on with this? I attempted to approach and was held back by the firemen. Why is she covered? Is she ok? "Boo! Can you hear me!" I didn't hear a reply. The firemen pushed me back again as I tried to press forward to check on the safety of my Latina.

A large red and yellow machine was pulled from the firetruck. It truly looks like an industrial size pair of machine scissors. The machine was cranked up and the man held it by the handles on the red and yellow base. When he did something to it the two metallic blades sticking out of the base opened and closed like a large scissor. Were these the Jaws of Life?

They yanked out the windshield with a shower of shattered glass spraying the ground and cut the post connecting the roof to the door between the windshield and front passenger door. They did the same thing with the middle post connecting the roof to the door between the front and back door. The Jaws of life sounded like a chainsaw as it revved up when cutting through the steel truck then the sound faded to a hum as it idled. The same process was performed on the other side of the truck. The golden blanket covering Latina was to keep the fragments and debris from getting all over her. The firemen peeled the now metal colored roof off like a sardine top.

Latina was fitted with a neck brace and pulled out of the convertible Blazer and placed on a stretcher. She was led to the ambulance and hoisted on the platform in the back. I attempt to hope in the back but was quickly redirected. I was allowed to ride up front in the passenger seat of the ambulance as we drove away to the hospital.

I called my moms. I called Latina's brother and whimpered my way through telling him we'd been in an accident. I was a mess not knowing Latina's condition. I couldn't give her brother much information other than what hospital we were being taken. Once at the hospital I was taking to be observed. I checked out ok.

My moms showed up and we embraced. Latina's family showed up and I broke down. I started apologizing and begging for forgiveness. I was reassured that it wasn't my fault and it was an accident. I hadn't seen her since she was put in the back of the ambulance. I wasn't her family so I had no say in getting to her.

The doctor came into the waiting room and let us knows she would be out shortly. Latina was pushed out on a wheel chair with her arm in a sling. She'd busted her elbow but other than that she was alright. We kissed and everyone went home.

We later found out that the guy who hit us was running from the police because he'd just robbed a bank. His attempt at getting rich quick changed the course of our lives forever. I had insurance on the truck and I was ready to get paid. Latina and I got a lawyer and when all was said and done she was given a settlement and so was I.

I took the money I got and found the largest and what I considered safest SUV I could find. I bought a white and gold 2000 Ford Expedition Eddie Bauer edition. All-wheel drive, peanut butter leather, factory chrome rims and a sun roof. I tinted it out and threw some slam in the back. I was looking like a million bucks and rolling like a boss.

School was continuing to get better for me. I'd schedule my classes so I would have long days. My junior year I told myself I could make the President's list. I made the dean's list so many times but would miss the presidents list by having 1 B on my report card. I was more determined than ever to make straight A's and for no other reason than to prove it to myself. I took 18 credit hrs. that semester.

I told myself everyday of that semester "It's yours if you want it but you got to earn it. It's not what you do but how you do it". School was never hard to me so much as time consuming. If I could keep my focus I would make the president's list.

While sitting in the library I was approached and asked if I wanted to take some pictures. I agreed. I was passed a "Calumet College" t-shirt and was paraded around to various locations in the school and asked to pose. I did. At the end of the session I was asked to read over and sign a release form. I read it and signed it.

At the end of the semester I was excited because I knew I'd done it. I knew I gotten all A's on every paper, test, and presentation in every class. I made the President's list! A perfect 4.0 GPA. My determination got stronger. My self-esteem grew.

I began thinking that I can do anything I put my mind to when I focus. I didn't think anything could make the feeling of accomplishment any better. Calumet College of St. Joseph turned me into a thinker, evaluator, strategist, and believer in myself. My mother was calm when I told her the news. She kept me humble by saying "see what you can do when you put your mind to it". I do and I did.

Like usual in the summer time we rode around and smoked weed. The sunroof in the Expedition was open. The sun was beaming through the hole in the roof. We were 3 deep as I was with June and Playboy. Playboy was in the passenger seat. We rode pass 46th and Broadway and Playboy went ballistic. "Go back, D, go back" he hollered as he bounced in his seat. "You didn't see that" he asked me. I didn't and I thought he was talking about a girl. He bounced in his seat and kept repeating himself, "just go back, you'll see".

I went back around the block and came back up Broadway. There it was! Standing about 20 feet tall was the largest picture of myself I'd ever seen. I was on a billboard! I was the new face of Calumet College of St. Joseph. It overwhelmed me. I was in awe.

How could this be possible. I'd been caught up in the hood mentality for so long that accomplishing my goals and being successful never seemed like something I could do. Every time I made leaps and bounds in my life Calumet College was behind it. The billboard was just my face and hands in perfect clarity with the school's name and phone number with the phrase "You Can".

I went home that afternoon and told my mother that I was the new face of the college. She quickly gave me her polaroid camera and told me to go back to the billboard and take a picture. I ran back out the house to the billboard and took several pictures.

Within a month of my first billboard I was all over Northwest Indiana. I had full page newspaper ads in all of the major papers, I was on the cover of the college's planners, up and down every major highway, and in the movie theater ads before the trailers began to play. Everywhere I looked I could see my face along with the motto "You Can". I knew it was time for a true change in my life.

I had friends coming out of jail saying they saw my picture in the paper and it wasn't because I was wanted for a crime. They would tell me that they wouldn't tell people they knew me. They wanted me to do something that hadn't been done in the hood, and that was to be legit. Real head busters would tell me if I had a problem on the street to let them know and they would handle it for me. I was feeling like a made man. All I had to do was play my role.

My friends were true to their word. If I brought up an issue, they would make sure the problem went away. I learned to watch my words because words have meaning. My words could cause harm to someone else. From that moment on I learned to speak with purpose or not at all.

I was always trying to emulate what I saw in the street, as that was all I knew. Everyone in the street who is about that life was trying to emulate me. I figured out quickly that I influence too. Once I showed and proved that going to school wasn't lame and it could lead to advantages, the streets followed me. My boys were going back to school to get their GED's. Some even got into college. I was the face of my college and I was not going to make them look bad. They put me in a spotlight that I would not let myself dim. Well, at least I thought.

During my senior year of college I was on top of my grades. I did everything I needed to do to be successful. I was a mentor for the inaugural men's basketball team. I had every last one of the players on my mentor's list. One of my duties was to make them comfortable with school. I was the go to for all things college when it came to them. If they were having any complications with school I was the listening ear and guide for them to get them back on track.

I'd formed a good bond with the team. We would go out to strip clubs at night and party. I was helping some of the more street team members understand that they have a real opportunity to move forward in life. Everything can change for the best if you want it bad enough. I liked my role as mentor.

I guess I'd gotten bored and needed to feel the street. I had a job working in the school system. I worked for 2 different schools at the time. I'd spend half of my day at one school and after lunch I'd travel across the town to the other school. I went home early one day for lunch. I sat in the driveway smoking a blunt with the windows down and sunroof cracked. I had my music up and the mood was how it needed to be. I then saw a geeker that owed me money from over a year ago. The last time we had a transaction he wanted some credit for $100 of work.

He was a good and loyal customer at the time so giving him some credit wasn't a big deal to me. He had a beautiful wife. She was perfect chocolate brown with long natural black hair flowing. Her body was perfect, it was too bad he turned her out on dope.

She worked at one of the bars on 25th Ave. as a bartender. They would call me after the bar closed. I'd go to the bar and she'd give me free drinks. After I was full she'd dig in the cash register and give me $200 for some work. I loved these geekers. They always had cash, at first. They got really strung out and their money flow changed. I should have seen it coming the way they spent money but I was blinded by the money. My kindness was used for a weakness.

They always paid their debt until the last time. They had moved to Indianapolis and ran off with my money. It was probably about a year when I saw him again as I sat in my truck smoking. There he was coming from my left. I called him over and he came happily. His smile changed quickly when I asked for my money. I guess he thought I forgot.

He got upset and tried to brush me off but I wasn't going for that bullshit and threated to whoop his ass if he didn't give me my money. I wasn't even selling crack anymore but he owed me and I wanted my money. I gave him an hour to get my money and he agreed. He continued his walk across the street and knocked on the door of the brick house.

The brick house was sandstone colored and one level. The woman that lived there was a free spirit. Often there were people over there drinking, smoking bud, and crack. I'd go over there and kick it with the old heads but usually just to see the woman. She was my mother's age and she enjoyed getting high and drunk.

She would also have company with men for a few ends to fill her pockets. She was the first nympho I'd ever met. It was known by everyone in the neighborhood who smoked work that I was the dope man. I would sit at her house sometimes because I knew geekers would come and want some work. Mostly I just wanted her to get high so she could give me some head or maybe more.

I found out the woman across the street smoked dope before my brother was killed. He and his friends were selling her work before I learned the game. He would tell me stories about how she would suck all their dicks for crack. I always wanted to fuck her as a boy but she wasn't messing with me like that.

She had a big ass that looked so soft. Her tits weren't big but just right. She often wore wife beaters with no bra and the wife beater would hold her chocolate tits tight. Her nipples would poke against the beater and outline her whole areola. A piece of side tit would fall out from time to time. My little dick would get hard. I would hang around and take a mental pictures when a tit did show itself. I was a horny teen. When I came back to the G, I was grown.

The first time we got down was when I had my Black Blazer. I was making moves and she was one of the first people I tried to manipulate with work. She manipulated me more. She called me over one night. She came out the house in a bathrobe wrapped around her like a trench coat. She was feeling good and asking me for some credit.

She then opened the robe to expose the fact that she was butt naked. Like a horny teen, I grabbed the tits I had so lusted over on the nights I used my mental pictures to fantasize about her. I was instantly turned on by how soft she was. Her skin was supple. My mind left my body and all the blood in my brain had traveled down to my dick. I was willing to give her whatever she wanted in that moment.

She told me to pull off and find a spot. She unzipped my pants and dug in for my dick as I was bending blocks to the school, tugging on me and moaning. We pulled up behind the middle school a short way away and I backed into the cut. I turned off the lights and she laid the seat all the way back so she was lying flat on her back in the passenger seat.

The robe came off and I began licking her nipples which she wasn't feeling. She told me to put the rubber on and fuck her. I complied. I crawled over the armrest and tried to put it in but she had the tightest pussy I'd ever felt. After some positioning, it was on and I was fucking the woman. I came quickly. She asked for her payment as I drove her back home. She and I had a relationship like that for years.

The woman across the street kept company so when the geeker who owed me money went to her house after our confrontation, it was nothing special. She let him in and her white screen door closed behind him. After about 30 minutes he left her home. As he walked back past me he started mugging me. I got mad.

He was staying a few houses down from me and when he got in front of his home he stopped. Looking my way, he folded his arms and began staring at me. I turned the key in the ignition and sped out the driveway. I dipped in and out of the street for 2 houses and parked my Expedition in the middle of the street, blocking off traffic.

I hopped out hyper and got in his face. He was unfazed as I tried to escalate the confrontation to a fight. I boiled with rage, fist clinched, and charged up for a fight. His expression never changed. Before I knew it 5 police cars pulled up out of nowhere.

The police came from all streets and surrounded us. Bronson was a well-known police officer who worked the GRIT unit. GRIT was a gang and drug unit. We called them the jump out boys because they would ride in unmarked, normal every day, cars in a caravan. They'd pull up and jump out in regular clothes with badges. They were all in marked police cars this time.

Bronson was smoking a cigar. He approached us. The geeker then became an Oscar deserving actor. "He jumped on the hood of my car waving a gun and threaten to kill me and my family! My wife and kids were in the car. He tried to kill us!" My mouth dropped and my heart sank to my stomach.

I was handcuffed 2 houses down from my house. Bronson asked me if I had a gun. I told him I did but I didn't do what he just told you. He asked the geeker to describe my gun. "It's a grey gun with a black pistol grip. I think it's a Ruger" he told the detective. He described it perfectly. It's levels to understanding and at that time I didn't realize showing my gun to everyone was a bad idea. It was often on my lap as I made hits. I'd walk around the hood with my holster on showing off my chopper.

Bronson asked me where the pistol was. I told him it was in the armrest. I then remember I had about a quarter ounce of bud in plain sight. He went to the truck, door still open from when I jumped out to confront the geeker. He opened the armrest and got the pistol. "Do you have a license for this pistol", he asked? I told him it was in my wallet in my back pocket. He retrieved it and pulled out the pink gun permit. "Is this your pistol?" he asked. "Yes," I replied. "Is this registered in your name," was the question that confused me.

I stuttered as I tried to figure out the question. "No, it's not registered in my name", I told him confused. The other officers were passing the gun around among themselves. They were mumbling about the pistol grip and neon green fiber optic site on the tip of the barrel of blue steel.

"Have the registered owner come get it if you want it back", I was told. Damn! This is the second gun the police have taken from me. I should have stayed at work. I'm about to go to jail because the police don't believe I didn't jump on the hood of his car and threaten his family.

Across the street was a white house that is a duplex. It had been abandoned for a while. The neighbor to that house would cut the grass to keep the yards looking nice. He had been cutting the grass and witness the whole demonstration from the time I dipped out of my driveway until now.

He stopped cutting grass and walked across the street to where we were standing. He pulled a badge out to reveal he was an officer also. He was updated with what the complaint was and what allegedly I had done. "I've been here the whole time and this young man didn't pull out a gun or jump on the hood of his car," he told Bronson. He told him that the geeker and I were arguing but no one threw a punch. I was uncuffed.

The officer who saved me pulled me to the side. "Don't you go to Calumet College of St. Joseph? You're the one in the paper and on the billboards. I graduated from that college. Why are you acting a fool over here? You know better. Go home," he told me. I didn't know this man but he knew me. He was disappointed in my actions and I could see it in his face.

I learned that day that you never know who knows you or your people. Perception is everything. I was not only representing myself but everything else that I am perceived to be. This is chess and I was playing checkers. If I wanted to balance both worlds I'd have to think about how I move before I move.

I went home and backed into the driveway. I began thinking about how I could have gone to jail over a debt and I wasn't even selling dope anymore. I could have lost my job and possibly fail a semester of college if that had happened. I looked down and there was my bag of bud sitting in plain site exactly where I left it.

I was relived they didn't find that because if they had found the weed I would have gone to jail too. I sat back and rolled a blunt. As I inhaled deeply I knew I was blessed or maybe I was being guided to do something bigger than I could understand. The way the officer came to help me out from nowhere. How did the drug police not see that bag of bud? I've had more than several instances up to that point that were unexplainable but came out in my favor.

I went to the gun store and bought my 3rd Ruger the same day they took the other one. I bought the same P-90 Ruger but this time I got a black one. The last 2 blue ones got took. I was learning to keep information close to heart. I didn't need to get back into the street. That geeker must have called the police from the lady across the streets house when he went there after leaving me from the first confrontation. I fell right into his trap, that's why he was staring at me. I had to do better, I would do better.

Mikeo

Mikeo was a real problem for a lot people that didn't like how he moved in the streets. He was the type of guy that didn't listen to much bullshit. He'd call you out for lying or fronting. I had learned that you never know what might happen if you got in the car with him.

I was usually ready for whatever if we started touring the city. Mikeo was like a brother to me from the time I came back to the G. He let me get money in his spot and he scared most niggas. Mikeo would fight or shoot it didn't matter to him. He kept an arsenal of guns and he had cars all around the city in different locations. The niggas on 20 block were a different breed. They were savages and I liked it. They held the block down and choked all the air out of it. All of them were feared and notorious.

When I was still living in Michigan City, I had come to the G on the train. Loco had a Chevy Caprice. We went to 20 block 4 deep. I was in the passenger seat. June was behind me and Playboy was in the back behind Loco.

Loco had flipped from folks to Vice Lord when he moved to the East Side from Miller. Loco wasn't respected for flipping and the niggas on 20 block gave him hell. When we pulled up on the block there were 10 gangster ass niggas in the street drunk and yelling. As soon as we stopped a nigga named Jock reached in the car and began asking "Who the fuck is you" to Loco first. He told him, "I'm Loco". Jock looked at me and said, "What's up Lil Ralph". He looked at June and said, "What's up Lil Baldy".

Then he focused on Playboy. "Who the fuck is you", he asked. Playboy responded with his name, "I'm Playboy." "What the fuck is a Playboy?" Where you from? Why you on the block?" He screamed every word. Spit was flying out his mouth as he demanded to know why we were on the block. Playboy told him, "I'm Playboy. I'm from 16th. We came to see Mikeo". "What the fuck is a Playboy", he slurred. "What's the five points of the star" he insisted Playboy tell him or get violated.

Jock pulled out a pistol and leaned back in the car. The look of terror came across Playboys face and Loco's too. This was the first time I'd seen Loco shook. "What's the five points of the star?" he screamed again. Playboy started naming them then he said "loyalty," and that is not a point of the star.

Jock took his pistol and hit Playboy in the forehead as he sat in the backseat, crying. Up front next to me Loco began asking me what the points were as he knew he'd be next. I was telling him as Jock was halfway in the window yelling. "What the fuck is a Playboy?"

He repeated that phrase 5 or 6 times and every time he repeated that phrase he'd hit Playboy with the pistol. I told Loco to pull off. Jock heard me and stated, "If you pull off I'll shoot you in the back of the head" to Loco. Loco was repeating the points of the star I had just told him under his breath.

The goons had gathered around the car to watch Playboy get pistol whipped. Mikeo came out of the crowd and told Playboy to fight back, "Fight, ain't no bullets in the gun!", he yelled over Jock. Mikeo pulled Jock out of the car and Playboy rolled up the window. Jock broke free and open the unlocked door. "What the fuck is a Playboy", as he hit him with the pistol.

After every blow to Playboy's head the pistol would clank against the back window. They pulled him out the car again. I told Playboy to lock the door. I asked Loco to pull off. He put the car into gear and we got out of there.

I learned a lot from that incident. Loco wasn't as hard as he thought. Playboy wouldn't fight for his own life. I wasn't the friend I thought I was and neither was June. None of us did anything to stop that from happening.

I know we were all scared and didn't want to piss Jock off more. We went back to Playboys house that night and we all checked ourselves for not standing up like real niggas should. It started with me taunting Playboy. His face was bleeding and knots were swelling. The skin under his eye was busted. He'd just been pistol whipped but I took that opportunity to speak on it. "How will you expect me to fight for you if you won't fight for yourself?"

I had never seen my niggas so out of it. No one wanted to speak. Maybe I was over compensating for the fact I didn't do anything either. I had my .22 revolver in my pocket the whole time. I was afraid if I shot him we'd be gunned down from the crowd. June and I were left alone because of the strength of our brothers. I didn't want problems with them 20 block boys.

I was back in the G, I knew how to operate around Mikeo and all the 20 block boys. Anything could jump off on the block or riding with Mikeo. We had formed a bond and he knew I was down for anything. Every now and then he'd test my nuts. The first time I realized I was being tested it was too late.

It was after midnight and we were riding around looking for geekers to sell to, we pulled up on the End. Mikeo asked me if I had my chopper on me. I shook my head, yes. We stopped on Massachusetts St. and parked. He asked if I had some work on me. I shook my head, yes.

We got out the car and posted up on the porch of a red house that had many stone steps leading up to the door. The steps were painted red and old. Most of the paint had flaked exposing the greyish brown concrete beneath it. We sat on the steps and I knew we were in front of Lil Daddy's spot. We sat there for about an hour selling our work to the geekers as they walked up to us.

A female came to the door screaming at us and telling us to leave. "Bitch fuck you! Get your ass back in the house before you get fucked up too! Where your brother at?" he growled. "Das. My brother didn't have nothing to do with your brother getting killed. Stop shooting at my brother. He didn't have nothing to do with it", she pleaded.

I put my gun on my lap because I was ready for whatever came next. Hell, we were stealing their crack heads and selling dope at their spot. Mikeo motioned for me to get in the car. They yelled back and forth at each other for a while. The tires screeched as we pulled off into the night. Mikeo saw I was ready, he trusted my judgement. He proved that to me as I stopped him from killing at least 2 of my friends. Off the strength of my words and loyalty to my friends he spared their lives.

One afternoon, Mikeo was in my hood, behind the cul-de-sac was a field. The field separated the elementary school from the middle school. The schools sat on a hill on the field. There was a track, football field, baseball field, and basketball court in between the schools. When standing in the circle we were in the middle of both schools just off to the side. The hill prevented us from seeing the track and football field. The circle had a lining of trees that we'd park under in the summer to get relief from the sun.

Nothing major was happening and we were just standing around politicking. Leaves started falling off the trees. We looked up as that was unusual. More leaves fluttered down followed by the wiz of bullets. We couldn't hear any gun shots, but the wiz of a bullet is undeniable. As the bullet spins through the air it makes a noise. We all ducked down. Was someone shooting at us?

I ran up the hill and saw 2 niggas at the edge of the woods across the field shooting in our direction. They could not see us from there vantage point but never the less they were shooting at us. Mikeo asked if I had my chopper. I told him, "Yes!" We hopped into his grey primed Delta 88. The car had black tinted windows and triple gold Daytons. He peeled out and took off up the dirt hill onto the field. Grass, dirt, and rocks spit out the back as we sped towards the ones shooting. They split up as we got close. One went towards the elementary school and the other went towards the street. We followed the one with the rifle.

We were on the playground of the elementary school dodging swings and sliding boards as we chased down the shooter. He ran around the back of the school. We hit the street and came around the front of the school. The shooter had stopped running as he probably thought we left or gave up but we didn't.

When the car came up the driveway of the loading ramp the shooter stopped in his tracks. Mikeo jumped out the car and pointed the pistol at the shooter who was about a football field away from us. "Put the gun down" he yelled like the police. The shooter was frozen in place. Pop! One shot was fired and the shooter hit the ground. Mikeo ran up to the shooter, now laying on the ground and screaming in pain. Mikeo took his gun and ran back to the car. We sped off.

We hit a few blocks and pulled up on 20 block. We went down the alley behind the spot. Mikeo grabbed the 2 ½ - ton hydraulic jack. We jacked the car up and took the Dayton's off the Delta 88. We were so close the where the shooter got shot that by the time we'd put on the last factory tire, we could hear the police and ambulance coming to the scene. When the emergency vehicles went by I could see them. We got the last tire on and drove back past the scene and went back to the circle to finish chilling.

I was in and out of situations all the time. I was trying to balance work, school and the streets. In May of 2004, I graduated from college with my B. S. in Psychology and a minor in Media and Fine Art. I invited all the boys from the hood and they all came to see me cross the stage.

I had 15 gangster ass niggas in the stands rooting, hollering, and yelling when my name was called. None of us had ever been to a college graduation. All my family came too. You would have thought I was the most popular person at the school. The crowd erupted when I hit the stage.

My moms was so proud that she had a barbeque for me at the house after graduation. We had a tent big enough for 20 people. A port-a-pot with a sink so no one had to go inside the house. A full keg of beer and all my people. My back yard was full of my people. I was the glue that kept the hood together and that barbeque was the last time I saw all my niggas together and enjoying life.

Why

It has taken me several years to put these words on the page. I fought with myself about putting these stories in writing. I had to overcome my own "Hood Trauma". Hood trauma is when you have gone to war in an urban setting using nonmilitary guerrilla style tactics. Experiencing flashbacks, years later, which can be triggered by various stimuli leading to a release of uncontrolled emotions. Writing this book was therapy to me.

The experiences I overcame in my teenage years made me who I am today. I grew up in a neighborhood contaminated by the glare of the streets. I was all in due to the fact I didn't know any better. I was a product of my environment. I was the proverbial fish in the water... I didn't know I was wet until I left the hood and saw something else.

Once my perception changed so did my outlook on life. The expectation growing up in the hood is to live fast and die young. My brother was killed at 18 years old. I honestly didn't think I would live past 18. When I made it to 18, I didn't think I'd live to be 21. When I finally turned 21, I didn't think I would make it to 25. At 25 I knew I would be ok.

I don't know a person I grew up with that doesn't have a felony on their record except me. Over 20 people I grew up with have been murdered 10 of them in 1999 alone. I have witnessed lifeless bodies covered in blood dead on the street. Heard the screams of mothers after finding their child had been murdered, I have been the exception.

As the exception, I have seen and endured a lot and I have shared some of my experiences, but not all have been mentioned in this book. Names and places may have been changed or exaggerated.... Maybe or maybe not, if you know you know. I wish no malice, misrepresentation, or defamation on anyone in their feelings. You know too!

I have a responsibility to share the Life and Times of Dasism Lord because most of my guys are not here to tell it themselves. Mikeo, Playboy, and Loco were later murdered. That is another book. I was left by myself at the end as I was in the beginning. We were all young, dumb, and full of cum. I miss all my fallen soldiers. Their lives created a part of me.

I will show and prove until I see you all again. I'll end this story with the fact that if I can influence, so can you. But the question is what are you influencing? Are you progressing and moving forward or are perpetuating the same perspective that has kept you running in place? To see different, you must do different. We can be the change. I can be the change. You can be the change…YOU CAN!